x rays and gamma rays

DANIEL S. HALACY, Jr.

HOLIDAY HOUSE · NEW YORK

X rays can bring out not only hidden information but unsuspected
beauty, as shown in this picture of milkweed pods.

I haven't told anybody about my work. I just told my wife that I was working on something about which the people, after they would be told about it, would say "Röntgen apparently has gone crazy."

from a letter by Wilhelm Konrad Roentgen,
discoverer of X rays

contents

James L. Koevenig and Gerald R. Smith, University of Kansas

Thanks to X rays, here is proof that one snake literally did swallow its own tail. This immature blue racer was placed in an empty jar and in this forced circular position began to swallow as food what it may have considered to be another snake. The peristaltic waves of its intestine apparently drew its body into its own intestine farther and farther until the animal suffocated, the tail tip having first broken through the body wall. Biologists of several universities have examined the body and X ray pictures and declared it a genuine and probably unique occurrence. The two light spots are from weights that held the snake flat against the X-ray film.

8

1   the world of x rays

~~~~~~

Today, some three-quarters of a century from the time of their discovery, X rays are still as mysterious to most of us as their name signifies. Even though we may have been X-rayed and have the vague knowledge that this invisible radiation has many uses in medicine, industry, and science, we feel that there is still an air of black magic about it. For X rays cannot be seen, felt, heard, or otherwise detected by human senses. Professor Wilhelm Konrad Roentgen, the man who discovered the rays sometimes called by his name, wrote vaguely about seeing them on several occasions; scientists have reported that laboratory rats seemed able to detect X rays by means of their noses. In general, however, we cannot sense X rays naturally. Little wonder their discoverer called them unknown rays.

X rays were generated by man perhaps 20 years before he was aware of what he had done; as we shall see later, the first man to accomplish the feat did not know it. And even Roentgen, who did track down the "new kind of ray," stumbled onto it by chance. The discovery was an excellent example of the process of serendipity—discovery by a happy accident. Of course, as has been wisely said, chance greatly favors the man who is intellectually prepared to take advantage of his opportunities.

The fact that we cannot see X rays made their discovery difficult. But man uses many things he cannot see. The wind is among these, as are heat and radio waves. (Experiments seem to indicate, however, that some people can *hear* radio waves in the radar range.)

It was many years after the discovery of X rays before science knew definitely what they were. But that is neither surprising nor a condemnation of the scientists involved. After all, science did not yet know about the electron, or how to split an atom. Planck and Einstein and Rutherford had not yet shown that matter and energy were really different faces of the same basic building block of nature. And, as one early authority on X rays put it, men did not even know what gravity was but were able to live with its effects, and build science around it.

With X rays Roentgen could see the shadowy outline of a key hidden in a thick technical book. His unknown rays were also the key that opened the door in a few short years to a whole new scientific world—the world of nuclear energy. From Roentgen the strange invisible trail led to Antoine Henri Becquerel, the Curies, and radioactivity. Ernest Rutherford used radioactive streams to prove that atoms consisted of a relatively huge nucleus surrounded by whirling electrons. He was first to achieve nuclear reaction artificially, and the

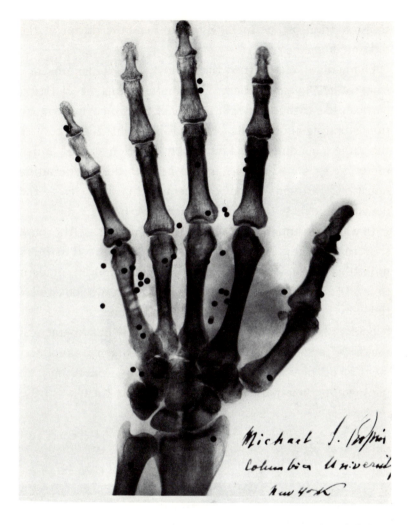

Burndy Library

A very early medical application of X rays. This historic photograph was made in February 1896 by the physicist Michael I. Pupin of Columbia University. It was made to help the surgical removal of more than forty gunshot pellets received in the hand of a New York attorney in a hunting accident. Professor Pupin's signature appears at the lower right. He had set up his own X-ray apparatus after getting information on the new discovery directly from a German physicist.

transmutation of one metal into another—the dream of the old-time alchemists.

Gradually it was learned that X rays, and the gamma rays from radioactive materials, were not streams of electrical particles like cathode rays, but waves of electromagnetic radiation vibrating much faster than visible light but otherwise the same phenomenon. This faster vibration carried much more energy, and pioneers in the field of this "penetrating radiation" learned—some of them with their lives—the devastating effects that came from unwise use.

It was unfortunate that many were ignorant of the facts concerning X rays in the early days of their use. It is more unfortunate that such ignorance is still found in modern times. It is strange too, for almost everywhere we look today there are applications of penetrating radiation.

Seldom has a new discovery been so quickly put to practical use as X rays. Within a few days of Roentgen's announcement of his new kind of ray, in fact, doctors were using it to photograph their patients and even to treat them.

X rays bring out the structure and beauty of a fish's bones and cartilaginous parts.

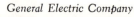

General Electric Company

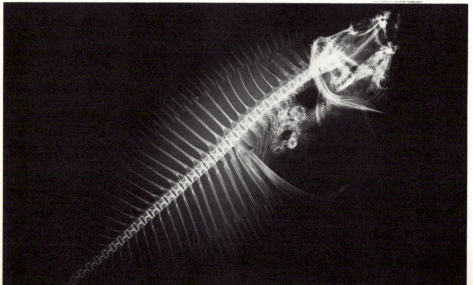

the energy of many uses

Industry too uses X rays to examine certain products. However, it was not until World War I that manufacturers began doing this, and only with World War II did they begin doing it on a large scale. Less known, but possibly as important, is the use of penetrating radiation in chemical processes to yield new and different products that cannot be made in other ways.

Various foods can also be preserved by being given doses of X rays or gamma rays, though the complete safety of this is still disputed. Such radiation processing may make it possible to keep foods for long periods of time without refrigerating them, and also to eliminate the dangers of eating such fare as undercooked pork. Another X-ray use is that of eradicating pests which destroy crops or cause disease.

The versatility of X rays, in old fields and new, is remarkable. Most sciences and many new technologies make use of them. Examples are astronomy, laser science, and space navigation. X rays are used in a variety of equipment, including microscopes, fluoroscopes, gauges, counters, and stereoscopic moving pictures. X-ray diffraction, the bending of the rays by certain crystals, opened a whole new field of measurement and analysis. The same was true for X-ray spectroscopy, which almost immediately led to the system of atomic numbers. A gauge of the importance of X-ray photography— or radiography, as it is called—may be seen from the fact that more film is used for this purpose than for all the black and white picture-making we amateur photographers indulge in.

These four cylindrical pistons put crystalline materials under intense pressure. The high-intensity X-ray tube in the metal housing running horizontally through the press shows up the readjustment of atoms in the crystal as pressure and heat increase in the sample.

As with many other blessings, there are dangers as well. Along with intentionally created and beneficial X radiations, there are those which are not so desirable. The coming of nuclear energy brought with it hazards of gamma radiation in fallout from atom bomb tests and also from nuclear-power reactors. Part of this radiation is much like that generated in medical and industrial X-ray tubes. Except, that is, for its greater penetrating strength. Nobel invented dynamite and many another powerful explosive, thinking mostly of its constructive applications. Yet he died with the knowledge that his inventions had killed thousands upon thousands. The same danger exists in penetrating radiation, and we must guard against improper use that would result in a world unfit for human use. Roentgen received a Nobel prize. He also lived to see his invention cause the death of human beings. It is certain, however, that the good done by X rays far exceeds their harm.

X and gamma rays, then, represent a mixed blessing for us humans. To make the most from the good they offer, we should know the dangers as well. In this book we shall look at both sides of the coin.

To understand X and gamma rays we must first learn what they are; not particles like alpha and beta rays but waves of electromagnetic energy. Surprisingly, they are close kin to the visible light waves that we are much more familiar with. This knowledge is the result of many years of scientific detective work, laboratory experiment, and great good fortune. Perhaps the easiest way to roll back the shadowy veil of mystery that hides X rays is to conduct some simple experiments with the radiation itself. Such experiments can be done safely and inexpensively by amateurs *if* they are under the careful supervision and guidance of those who are familiar with the dangers and the safeguards.

Our book begins with an explanation of electromagnetic waves.

2   the electromagnetic spectrum

The genius of Albert Einstein seems to have best pinned down the material things that make up our universe. His monumental equation $E=Mc^2$ includes energy, matter, and light. Energy, Einstein tells us, is equivalent to matter. Energy is matter "unfrozen." The full range of energies of different types is called the electromagnetic spectrum; all of them travel with the speed of light. At 186,282 miles per second, this is the fastest that anything can travel in our universe.

A piece of coal when burned gives off heat, and heat is radiant energy. A candle gives light, and light is radiant energy. Our sun emits radiant energy in the form of light, and a square mile of sunlight weighs only one pound. To give an idea how much energy that represents, one writer estimates it would cost us $400,000,000 to create a pound of man-made light.

The entire spectrum of electromagnetic energy has been described as consisting of 60 "octaves," with each octave doubling in frequency. Visible light makes up only one of these 60 octaves. The octave made up of the highest frequencies of radiation—and consequently the most energetic or powerful—is the one we shall be concerned with in this book. Because they are invisible, and detectable only with special instruments, X rays and gamma rays were the last part of the spectrum to be discovered. Man had to begin his study of radiation somewhere near the middle of the spectrum.

Newton's rainbow

Visible light is the only part of the spectrum that man can see, and he gains about three-fourths of his knowledge of the environment through sight. For millions of years men have been seeing but only recently have we begun to wonder about the nature of the light that lets us see. Much like fish unaware of the water surrounding them, we simply accept light as a fact of life. But slowly the more curious began to wonder—and to investigate.

The Greek philosopher Empedocles, born 500 years before Christ, knew enough about light to guess that it must have motion and travel at a fixed speed. Aristotle, born in 322 B.C., went further and theorized that the white or "pure" light from the sun was changed into colors because of contamination by earthly things.

The study of optics began early; in the ruins of Nineveh archaeologists unearthed a lens believed to be some 4,000 years old. By the time of Ptolemy, who was a Greek or

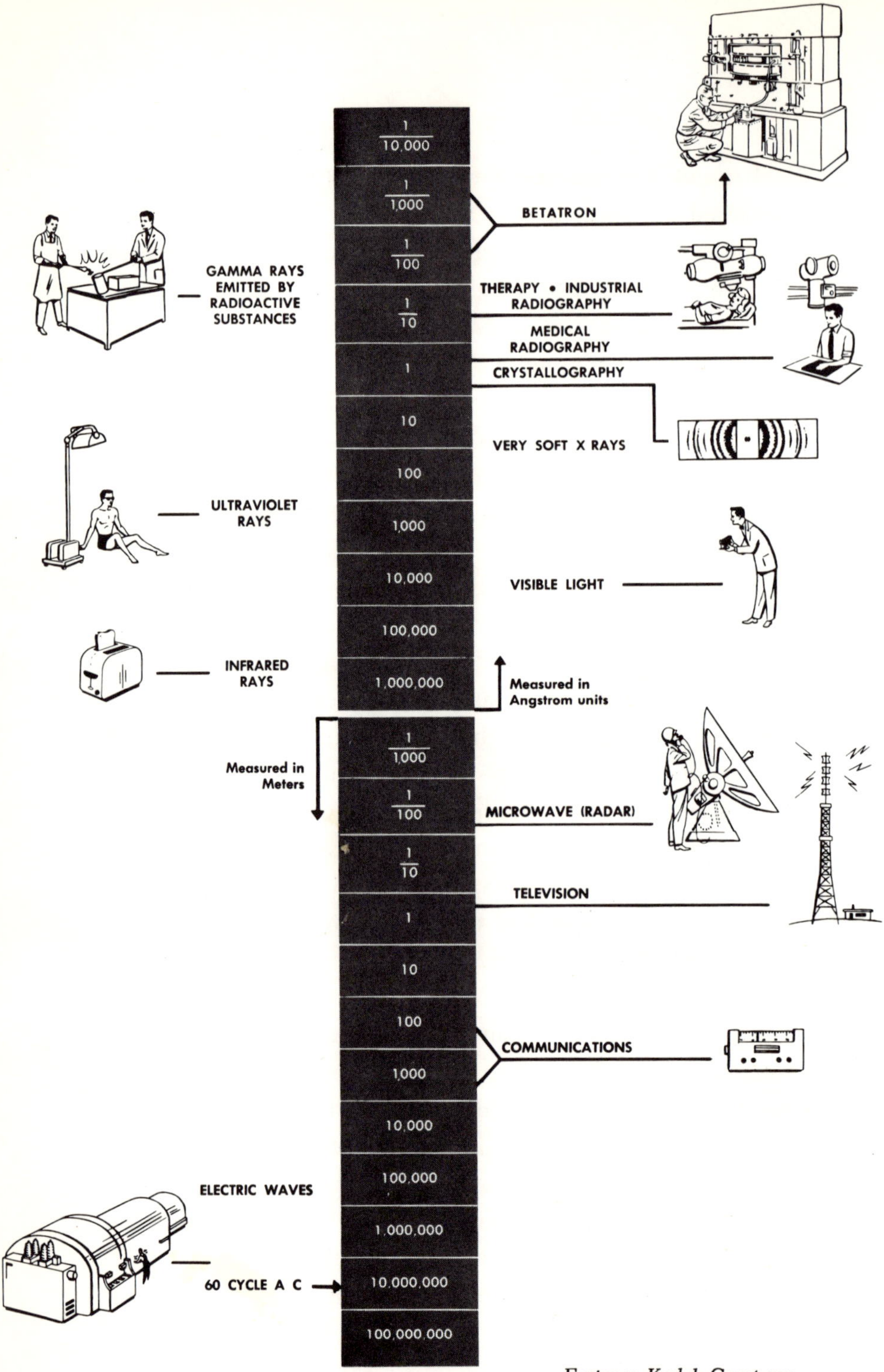
1/10,000
1/1,000
1/100
1/10
1
10
100
1,000
10,000
100,000
1,000,000
BETATRON
GAMMA RAYS EMITTED BY RADIOACTIVE SUBSTANCES
THERAPY • INDUSTRIAL RADIOGRAPHY
MEDICAL RADIOGRAPHY
CRYSTALLOGRAPHY
VERY SOFT X RAYS
ULTRAVIOLET RAYS
VISIBLE LIGHT
INFRARED RAYS
Measured in Angstrom units
Measured in Meters
1/1,000
1/100
1/10
1
10
100
1,000
10,000
100,000
1,000,000
10,000,000
100,000,000
MICROWAVE (RADAR)
TELEVISION
COMMUNICATIONS
ELECTRIC WAVES
60 CYCLE A C

Eastman Kodak Company

The electromagnetic spectrum.

perhaps an Egyptian astronomer in the second century after Christ, optics was flourishing, although there were serious errors on the part of Ptolemy. He believed, for example, that the eye sent out rays of light which illuminated objects so that we could see them. Perhaps this is understandable in a man who also thought the earth was the center of the universe.

The Arabian scientist Alhazen, born in 965, corrected many wrong beliefs about optics. Alhazen correctly pointed out that light originated in the sun or other luminous objects and was reflected from what we saw. He also constructed curved mirrors and even a crude pinhole camera.

Leonardo da Vinci was among the early scientists who were interested in light. He had observed rainbows and wondered at them, as many men before him had done. But Da Vinci was one of the first to study the "artificial rainbow" created by passing a beam of light through a glass prism. Da Vinci was famous in his own time for his great paintings, but his scientific discoveries he carefully concealed in his mirror writing. This was a secret code he used to prevent his work from being attacked by those who considered science akin to witchcraft. It was many years before the world learned all his findings.

No one is certain who invented the telescope, but Galileo, born in 1564, built a series of telescopes beginning in 1609, and the sciences of astronomy and optics took a tremendous stride forward from this. Galileo also tried to measure the speed of light, but was unsuccessful.

In 1642, more than 30 years after Galileo had startled the scientific world with his discovery of the mountainous and pitted surface of the moon, one of the world's greatest

Galileo Galilei,
from an old print.

scientists was born. His name was Isaac Newton, the man
we usually picture watching an apple fall to earth and being
thus stimulated to discover the laws of gravity. (No one is
really sure about that apple.) In addition to this great con-
tribution, Newton also worked out the useful binomial
theorem and the calculus in mathematics. We are more interested now, however, in his studies of light.

In thinking through his gravitational theory Newton naturally would be concerned with astronomy. And since telescopes are important in his field it is no surprise that he began to construct these instruments for himself. While studying the passage of light through his lenses, he was bothered by something called "chromatic aberration," the distortion of light beams at the edges of the lens to create fringes of color. As a result of his studies, Newton decided that nothing could be done to eliminate this troublesome factor, and he turned to mirrors instead of lenses. As it turned out, he was wrong about chromatic aberration, and later workers showed how two lenses could be put together to create anastigmatic lenses and eliminate the distortion. But Newton's work nevertheless led to two great discoveries: the reflecting telescope and a true science of optics.

The light that reaches us from the sun is colorless—white light as we call it. But since the first man saw a rainbow, there has been evidence that this white light actually included an infinity of colors. The sun in its inferno of hydrogen fusion produces light containing the whole color spectrum. Only when objects here on earth reflect certain wavelengths of light and absorb others do we perceive color. Since the waves of different colors are "bent" in different amounts when they pass through something that is denser than air, moisture in the air breaks the white light into the beautiful ring of color bands, each droplet acting as if it were a tiny prism. Newton, who had observed rainbows and the halo of light sometimes visible around the moon and knew what caused them, went further than Da Vinci in using a glass prism to produce a tiny rainbow in his laboratory. A round beam of light was refracted, or bent, to form a long oval of many colors.

Newton selected the seven most distinct of these: red, orange, yellow, green, blue, indigo, and violet.

Before this time, few scientists knew that light was composed of colors from violet to red. Even then they were unaware of the different wavelengths, as these measurements of light are called. In 1690, 23 years after Newton's prism experiments, the Dutch scientist Christian Huygens published his "wave theory" of light. Light, he said, consisted of longitudinal waves somewhat like sound waves.

As had scientists before him, Newton believed that light was a stream of tiny particles traveling at very high speed. In fact, at one time in his investigations of light he suggested that the spin of such "corpuscles" or round balls of light might be what caused the different colors to curve through the air. Such a spin does account for the curve of a baseball.

This theory had some shortcomings, such as the fact that it could not explain why different colors of light were refracted to different extents when passing from air to water or glass. However, the corpuscular theory remained more popular than the wave theory, which did take care of the refraction puzzle by showing that short wavelengths would be bent more.

The particle theory was more accepted for what seemed a good reason: while the wave theory worked fine for water or glass, which was something solid enough to conduct waves, and even for air (which was still *something*, although much thinner than solids), it failed completely to explain the transmission of light through a vacuum. And light certainly did travel through the millions of miles of emptiness between stars and the earth.

With the simplest of equipment Newton made a great step forward in projecting the separated colors of white light. At the rear can be seen his small reflecting telescope, shown in more detail in the following picture. From an old print.

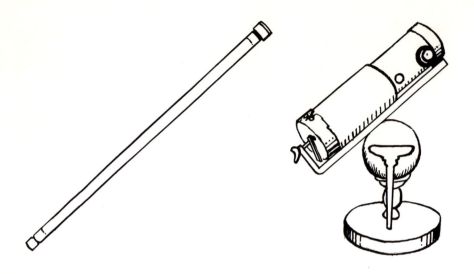

With tools like these the early investigators of light made new break-throughs in knowledge. Left, one of Galileo's refracting telescopes; right, Newton's second reflecting telescope. These historic instruments are now in museums.

the speed of light

Galileo, as mentioned earlier, tried to measure the speed of light. His experiments were simple: stationed far back from them, he watched two assistants with lanterns, each on a hill a long distance from the other. One uncovered his lantern and Galileo noted how long it took before he could see the second lantern uncovered, which was the signal saying that the second assistant had seen the light of the first. The experiment was repeated at increasing distances between the assistants but, because of the crudeness of the method, no reasonable estimate of the speed of light came from it.

Olaus Roemer, a Danish astronomer, in 1675 calculated the speed of light on a distance scale long enough to be very close to correct. Measuring the interval of time between the eclipses of Jupiter's innermost satellite when it was observed from a point of the earth's orbit that was nearest to Jupiter and a point of the orbit that was farthest from Jupiter, Roemer estimated a speed of 140,000 miles per second. The much longer path for the light to travel to the second position delayed it and gave him some idea of the speed. The inaccuracy was caused by an incorrect figure for the earth's orbit. When Roemer submitted his speed-of-light efforts to the French Academy of Sciences, they said, "It is absolutely impossible for anything, unless it be the Spirit of God, to attain such a speed as that on which the calculations of M. Roemer, the astronomer, are based."

However, in 1850, French physicist Jean Bernard Léon Foucault used a rotating-mirror system to calculate the speed of light at a figure of 187,000 miles per second. In 1879 Albert Abraham Michelson measured the speed of light in vacuum as 186,284 miles per second. Using such up-to-date equipment as the maser atomic clock, modern science has been able to correct this by only two miles to the presently accepted figure of 186,282 miles per second.

The fantastic speed of light, then, was a strong argument against the wave theory. While it was true that sound and

---

Olaus Roemer ingeniously used the motion of the earth around the sun to measure the speed of light. The vast distance between the two positions of the earth in its orbit was the key to this method.

Reprinted by permission from Science World, © 1960 *by* Scholastic Magazines, Inc.

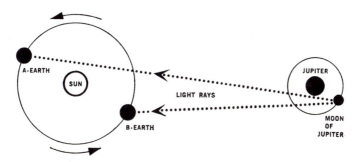

water waves existed, they traveled through matter—either solid substances, air, or water. To justify the wave motion of light through the vacuum of space, those who believed the theory had to rely on something they called the "ether." Further research seemed to prove that this mysterious substance did not exist, however. How, asked opponents of the wave theory, could light travel through a vacuum except in the form of tiny particles?

Even in 1801 when the English physician Thomas Young conducted experiments which seemed proof of the wave theory, the lack of a "medium" to carry the light waves prevented its acceptance. One of Young's experiments was to shine light through two closely spaced holes onto a screen. Instead of a bright area where the beams overlapped, the screen showed a series of light and dark bands, explainable only by assuming that light was composed of waves and not particles. However, these waves were not longitudinal but transverse, like the waves created in a rope when it is moved briskly up and down.

Young's experiments also gave an idea of the size of the light waves he theorized. Knowing the distance between the holes and measuring the distance between the alternating bands produced on the screen, he calculated that red light had a wave length of only about 0.000075 centimeter. Today we express light waves as "angstrom" units (named for Swedish astronomer Anders Jonas Ångström). An angstrom, or A, is one hundred-millionth of a centimeter. Red light is 7,700 A, and violet light is 3,900 A.

The proof that light waves were so very small was further argument for the wave theory, since now it was known why the light rays didn't fan out or bend around an ordinary object as sound and water waves do: light waves were far smaller than most objects they encountered. By 1816, however, the French scientist Augustin Jean Fresnel was able to prove that light *would* bend or travel around an obstruction if it was small enough. The bending of light around a solid object or around the edges of fine slits as it passes through is called diffraction. He made diffraction gratings, pieces of glass with fine lines scratched across them, very close together; these minute obstructions diffracted the waves slightly, producing a light spectrum. Slowly the particle theory of light gave way to the once-ridiculed wave theory. However, there was still an unsolvable riddle of how light waves traveled in a vacuum.

The colors of light are important clues in science. So important, in fact, that a number of elements have been discovered by the identification of their characteristic wavelengths or spectrum colors when they are vaporized by heat. Among the elements discovered by this method, called spectroscopy, are thallium, so named for its green color; cesium, which has a blue-green color; indium, which is in the indigo band of the spectrum; and rubidium, for the characteristic red line it produces in the analyzing instrument, the spectroscope. But some of the greatest scientific discoveries were to come in the invisible spectrum, that part of the electromagnetic radiation we cannot see at all.

invisible waves

The visible light spectrum that Newton showed us ranged from about 3,900 A to 7,700 A. It was not until 1799 that scientists detected electromagnetic waves outside this range.

In that year the English astronomer Sir William Herschel conducted a prism experiment much like that of Newton. However, he placed thermometers in the various colors of the spectrum to see which registered the highest temperature. Red light ran the mercury up the most, but surprisingly, when Herschel put a thermometer beyond the end of the red it went even higher. There was obviously a hotter radiation in the "infrared" or below-red range. To test the new waves, Herschel conducted experiments in which he found that invisible infrared waves behaved just as the visible part of the spectrum did. They could be reflected, refracted, and focused like visible light. It was these invisible rays that caused most of the heat from fire.

Two years after Herschel discovered infrared waves, a German physicist named Johann Wilhelm Ritter made another discovery beyond violet light. The violet end of the

The photograph on the left was shot on ordinary panchromatic film, the one on the right on infrared film. Notice that green foliage shows up lighter with infrared (especially noticeable in the tree), the blue sky registers darker, and the haze between the camera and the distant mountains disappears. *Eastman Kodak Company*

spectrum is cool; there were no hot waves beyond it in that direction, so Ritter had to use another detection method. Silver chloride blackens when exposed to light; this is the principle of photography, a photochemical reaction. Ritter placed some of the white silver chloride beyond the violet part of the spectrum, just as Herschel had placed his thermometer beyond the red end. Sure enough, the silver chloride darkened. In fact, it darkened much more than that placed in the blue or violet light. He had discovered ultraviolet (beyond-violet) light.

With more refined detection methods, ultraviolet rays were measured down to about 200 A. Working in the other direction with the Langley bolometer, invented by Dr. Samuel P. Langley of the Smithsonian Institution, the scientists established the existence of infrared waves at about 10,000,000 A. The electromagnetic spectrum was growing.

By now there was much experimentation being done with electricity and magnetism. Michael Faraday showed how these two forces acted together, and also how they interacted with light. Later, James Clerk Maxwell worked out the mathematics of Faraday's ideas. Maxwell's 1864 papers on electromagnetic waves theorized that there must be far longer waves than the infrared. A suitable vibrating electrical charge should result in such waves traveling at the speed of light.

Experimenters were not long in substantiating Maxwell's theory. In fact, claims have been made that Joseph Henry produced radio waves as early as 1842. Few authorities support this claim, but there are well-documented reports of demonstrations soon after Maxwell predicted the waves of electromagnetism. In 1866, for example, an American named Mahlon Loomis sent signals without wires a distance of about

As reproduced by the Saturday Review *from Mahlon Loomis' application*

The almost forgotten pioneer Mahlon Loomis made this sketch in his application for a United States patent on wireless communication. At the right a kite is tied to a branch on the log; the wire from the kite leads to an electrical recorder, the other terminal of which is grounded in water. Actually, as Loomis described it, the wire also kept the kite tethered.

18 miles between two kites sent up to an altitude of several hundred feet above ridges 2,000 feet high. From the somewhat unclear surviving records, he apparently relied on atmospheric static electricity rather than a battery. Unfortunately nothing came of this pioneering effort.

Several years later another American, Elihu Thompson, who was a science teacher at Philadelphia Central High School, produced sparks in his laboratory some distance from a spark-producing machine. And Sir Thomas Preece of England has been credited with achieving wireless transmission in 1885. However, it was not until 1887 and Heinrich Hertz's experiments in Germany that Maxwell's electromagnetic waves were both definitely produced and definitely identified.

As man began to harness electromagnetic radiation, science

revived the old question of how such energy was propagated through space. The old idea of an ether which conducted it was destroyed by the Michelson-Morley "ether-drift" experiments of 1887. In these experiments light was beamed in various directions to a reflector and its speed measured. Theoretically, if the light waves were conducted by the imagined ether in the universe, light would travel more quickly when beamed in the same direction as the motion of the earth than when sent out at right angles. The experiments showed no difference at all, and this was taken as proof that there was no ether.

It remained for the German scientist Max Planck to solve the riddle of the radiation of electromagnetic energy. Planck suggested that radiation, although a wave form, was also composed of very small units of energy, which he named quanta. One quantum was the basic unit of radiation. Planck's quanta depended on the wavelength, and the shorter the wavelength, the more energy it contained. Here at last was an explanation that satisfied all the critics once they understood the revolutionary concept of quanta of energy.

Both Newton with his corpuscle theory and Dr. Young with his wave theory were right. Electromagnetic radiation possessed the qualities of a wave and also those of a particle at the same time. The particle concept allowed for the travel of radiation through a vacuum; the wave nature accounted for all the observed optical effects.

Radio waves are longer than light waves, although they are also electromagnetic waves. Being longer, and traveling at the same speed, radio waves are lower in frequency than light waves. Science has detected waves in nature even far longer than these. These waves are so long that they are measured in seconds per cycle instead of cycles per second, and waves more than 100 seconds long have been measured.

Matter is electrical in nature, and when matter vibrates or oscillates it generates electromagnetic waves. These are so called because both electrical and magnetic fields are created, at right angles to one another. The electromagnetic wave is a transverse wave—a wave moving at right angles to the direction of the radiation. This is unlike sound waves, which move in the same direction as the sound in concentric ever-widening circles, or water waves, which also move in expanding rings, which can be seen when you throw a stone into a lake. An electromagnetic wave is something like two long ropes which are snapped up and down and horizontally to produce a series of ripples along their length at right angles to each other.

The amount of energy carried in an electromagnetic wave is in reverse proportion to the length of the wave. In other words, the very long waves of radio do not carry the energy of very short waves.

By 1895 the spectrum of electromagnetic radiation had been increased from the visible octave of the rainbow to many octaves; from the very short ultraviolet rays to radio waves millions of times that long. What of the spectrum beyond the ultraviolet, or had Ritter discovered all there was in that direction with his silver chloride? Soon two European scientists proved that there *was* very powerful radiation of far shorter wavelength than the ultraviolet. The discoveries came as Roentgen experimented with cathode rays, and Becquerel followed up Roentgen's work with radioactive substances. Their findings were X rays and gamma rays—the short, high-energy radiation so important in our world.

32

3 the discovery of x rays and gamma rays

X rays, named for the letter designating the unknown, were discovered quite by accident. This happened in 1895 in a German laboratory at the University of Würzburg, when Professor Wilhelm Konrad Roentgen noted a strange radiation emanating from a Crookes tube he was experimenting with. It is a strange quirk of fate that Sir William Crookes, the English chemist and physicist who invented the Crookes tube, did not also discover X rays. And neither did any of the many other researchers who experimented with the tube.

Sir William Crookes was born in London June 17, 1832, the year after Faraday invented the electric generator. At the age of 16 he entered the Royal College of Chemistry and began the study of that subject. However, he soon became more interested in spectroscopy. Analyzing selenium ores, he discovered the element thallium in 1861. Part of the delicate work with this new element involved weighing it in a vacuum to find its atomic weight. For some unknown reason the balance scale Crookes used moved erratically in the vacuum chamber, and he guessed that radiation pressure might be causing this motion. Finally, in 1875, he developed an instrument he called a radiometer, since it measured the radiation of sunlight. Still in use today, radiometers spin energetically when their black and white vanes are exposed to sunlight. Crookes thought light rays had substance and that their energy caused the motion of his vanes, even though that motion is not as simple as it appears.

In 1838 Michael Faraday, the great English scientist who fathered the electrical field, produced a brief discharge of electricity in a glass tube from which much of the air had been pumped out. Some 30 years later the German Wilhelm Hittorf gave the name cathode rays to this stream of electric

This is where it all began: Roentgen's laboratory at the University of Würzburg. *Burndy Library*

current in his experiments. Meantime, Heinrich Geissler, a German inventor, had developed an improved air pump and made vacuum tubes that were much better than Faraday had used.

In 1875 Crookes made an improvement on the Geissler tube. When a strong electrical potential was applied to the Geissler tube, luminescence occurred. The Crookes tube allowed a better study of this interesting phenomenon. This was in the days before electronic theory had been developed but it was obvious that there was a flow of radiation from the cathode, or negative terminal in the tube. Crookes showed with his new tube that these rays could be blocked out and cast a shadow on fluorescent material at the end of the tube.

As with his radiometer, he was able to turn a small mica wheel with the stream of cathode rays, a sort of electrical turbine wheel. Crookes did more than this. Using magnets, he deflected the stream of cathode rays. This convinced him that cathode rays were not electromagnetic waves but a stream of electrically charged particles.

Crookes kept photographic plates in the laboratory where he operated his electrical tubes. Once in a while these plates mysteriously were fogged and thus ruined, even when they were enclosed in protective containers. Crookes was seeing the work of a new kind of radiation, but unfortunately he did not know it. After all, no one even suspected the existence of the strange X rays during the 1880s. Eventually Crookes solved the problem of the ruined photographic plates simply by keeping them out of the laboratory. In so doing he left the discovery of X rays to Roentgen. Crookes was knighted in 1897. In 1903, still an active research physicist, he invented the spinthariscope, a device for studying radioactivity.

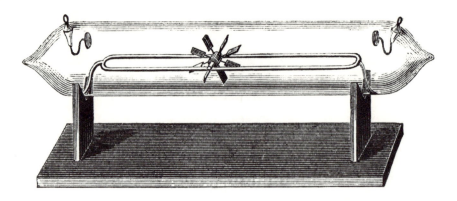

In this version of the Crookes tube the physicist showed that cathode rays could actually turn a wheel. Originally published in William Crookes' *Radiant Matter*, 1879.

Some time after Crookes had solved his fogged-plate problem, a scientist in America also came close to discovering X rays. Dr. A. W. Goodspeed, on February 22, 1890, accidentally made an X-ray photograph in Philadelphia. Like Crookes, however, Goodspeed did not realize what he had done. Years later, when he learned of Roentgen's amazing discovery, Goodspeed admitted this as he displayed the X-ray picture to an audience of scientists at the University of Pennsylvania:

"We can claim no merit for the discovery, for no discovery was made. All we ask is that you remember, gentlemen, that six years ago, day for day, the first picture in the world by cathodic rays was taken in the physical laboratory of the University of Pennsylvania."

the Roentgen rays

Wilhelm Konrad Roentgen was born in Lennep, Rhenish Prussia, on March 27, 1845, some 13 years after Crookes. He began his scientific career as a student of mechanical engineering but like Crookes soon changed his field and became a physicist. He came to the University of Würzburg in Bavaria with his teacher and soon headed the department of physics. In 1895, after 25 good but not spectacular years at the school, his lucky accident happened. This, remember, was some ten years after Crookes had ruined photographic plates in his laboratory with his cathode ray experiments.

On the eighth of November, Roentgen was experimenting with the Crookes tube, or the Hittorf tube, as he called it. Heinrich Hertz, who discovered radio waves, had also proved that cathode rays could penetrate thin aluminum foil. Philipp Lenard, whom Roentgen knew well, had built Crookes tubes fitted with foil "windows" to permit the cathode rays to emerge from the tubes so he could study their effects in air. These rays were known for a time as Lenard rays. Roentgen wondered if strong cathode rays might penetrate the glass itself.

Since the glow was quite faint at the end of the tube, he pulled the blinds to darken the room so he might better see the luminescence. He also wrapped the Crookes tube in black cardboard so that the greenish glow would be more noticeable. Roentgen got everything in readiness and turned on the electric power. No cathode rays were seen from the end of the tube, since it was covered. But at that instant Roentgen saw from the corner of his eye a glow somewhere across the darkened laboratory. Annoyed, he left off his experiment and went to see what it was that distracted him. On a table some distance from the Crookes tube was a sheet of paper he had coated with barium platinocyanide, one of the chemical compounds he had been studying for

37

fluorescence. Frowning, he looked about the room for the explanation and saw nothing but the Crookes tube. He walked back, puzzled because there were still no cathode rays to be seen at all. He shut off the power and looked over at the glowing sheet of paper. Slowly the glow faded until the room was in darkness again.

Here was something that made no sense. Shrugging his shoulders, he snapped the switch again and the Crookes tube hummed with electric current. And again, across the room, came the eerie greenish glow.

Later Roentgen was asked what he thought when this strange thing occurred. "I didn't think," Roentgen told his questioner, "I experimented." For almost two months he did experiment and what he found out seemed fantastic even to him.

Cathode rays could not be causing the glow across the room since they penetrated air for only a few inches. Instead there must be some kind of secondary emanation from the Crookes tube, a mysterious new radiation never before reported that was invisible and able to penetrate cardboard. Soon it was evident that it went through a thick book, and wood as well. Roentgen substituted rubber as a shield but the strange radiation went right through it too.

But the rays did not go through everything, Roentgen found. When he placed a box of laboratory weights between the Crookes tube and the coated paper, there was a faint shadow the shape of the wooden box, and inside it the darker shapes that were the round weights. For the first time, man was able to "see" through solid material. A similar situation turned up when the rays went through a book but not a key inside the book. And at last Roentgen placed his own hand

39

in the stream of mysterious radiation and saw on the coated paper the faint outline of flesh and the heavier outline of bones within.

Frau Bertha Roentgen feared that her husband was angry about something, until finally he confided his great secret to her. When she expressed disbelief, Roentgen took her to the

Smeary and unsharp though it is, this is a photograph of great historic importance. It was one of the first X-ray pictures sent by Roentgen to other scientists as proof that the rays actually penetrated opaque matter. It shows metal weights inside a closed wooden box.

Burndy Library

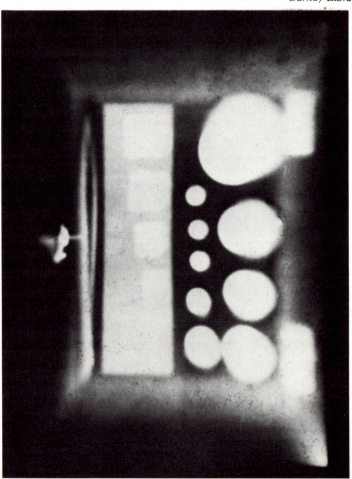

laboratory and demonstrated his mysterious rays. It was then that he made the first intentional X-ray photograph, one showing the bones of his wife's hand, and the two rings she wore.

By December 28 of 1895, just three days after Christmas, Roentgen submitted the first paper on his mysterious rays. Roentgen's paper was titled "Ueber eine neue Art von Strahlen," which means "On a New Kind of Ray." It was published in the journal of the Würzburg Physical Medical Society. Because he did not know what they were, he had named them X rays, or unknown rays. He reported on the many experiments he had conducted and reported many of the fundamental properties of the X rays. Only in the matter of reflection and refraction was he in error, since he did not know the conditions under which the rays would perform these things. It would remain for others at a later date to clear up the mystery and show that X rays obeyed the same laws of optics that applied to other electromagnetic radiation.

On January 6, 1896, the *Daily Chronicle* in London told its readers that "The noise of the war's alarm [trouble with Germany over South Africa] should not distract attention from the marvelous triumph of science, which is reported from Vienna. It is announced that Professor Roentgen, of the Würzburg University, has discovered a light, which for the purpose of photography, will penetrate wood, flesh, cloth and most other organic substances."

On January 23, 1896, Roentgen gave the first public demonstration of X rays. The crowning feat was the making of an X-ray photograph of the hand of Rudolph Albert von Kölliker, a venerable 80-year-old physiologist on the Würzburg faculty. Stunned, Von Kölliker made the following tri-

In February 1896, the same month that Professor Pupin made the X ray of a shot-filled hand shown earlier in this book, Dr. Gilman Frost at Dartmouth College directed the X-raying of a broken arm. Professor Edwin B. Frost, at left, timed the exposure. Because the basic apparatus was already available in laboratories everywhere, X-ray units were set up quickly as soon as news of the discovery reached around the world.

bute to his younger colleague: "In all the 48 years during which I have belonged to this society, I have never yet attended a session in which matters of such great moment were expounded as those we have heard today."

Proudly holding the X-ray picture of his hand, the aging Von Kölliker told the cheering audience that the new rays should henceforth be called Roentgen rays rather than X rays, in honor of their discoverer. Scientists tried to use this new name, but since Roentgen is not as easy to say, the original terminology prevailed. X rays they have been until this day, although the name Roentgen has been honored in technical terms applying to the radiation.

The January 30, 1896 issue of the *Nation* published a long article in tribute to Roentgen and pointed out the possibilities inherent in the rays:

> The importance of this discovery in its application to surgery as an aid to diagnosis in cases of disease or fracture of the bones is apparent. The photographs would reveal immediately and unmistakably the nature of the disorder without the long and often painful examination which the patient is now obliged to endure. In a case of complicated fractures another photograph can be taken after the bones have been set in order to ascertain whether the dislocation has been properly reduced or the broken parts have been rightfully replaced. The exact position of a bullet or the splinter of a shell can also be easily found without the use of a surgeon's probe. In all probability, the process can be perfected and modified so as to photograph the heart, lungs, liver, and other internal organs, and thus determine their precise condition.

The idea of "light rays" that could look right through clothes, skin, and flesh jolted the public. Lines from the third act of *Hamlet* that seemed to prophesy what Roentgen had done were recalled excitedly:

> Come, come, and sit you down; you shall not budge,
> You go not till I set you up a glass
> Where you may see the inmost part of you.

A photography magazine published a humorous comment on the prying X ray:

> The Roentgen Rays, the Roentgen Rays,
> What is this craze:
> The town's ablaze
> With the new phrase
> Of x-rays' ways.
> I'm full of daze,
> Shock and amaze,
> For nowadays
> I hear they'll gaze
> Thro' cloak and gown—and even stays,
> These naughty, naughty Roentgen Rays.

London's *Punch* magazine put it this way:

> We do not want, like Dr. Swift,
> To take off our flesh and pose in
> Our bones, or show each little rift
> And joint for you to poke your nose in.

A New Jersey legislator even introduced a bill prohibiting the use of X-ray opera glasses in theaters, and newspapers in London advertised X-ray-proof underwear! Perhaps the most fantastic "use" of X rays was that described in a New York newspaper: "At the college for physicians and surgeons, the Roentgen rays were used to reflect anatomic diagrams directly into the brains of the students, making a much more enduring impression than the ordinary methods of learning anatomical details."

"Look pleasant, please." Around the turn of the century this cartoon appeared in the old humor magazine *Life*. It is interesting that the artist, unaware of future findings, "predicted" that the sun emits X rays.

Despite all the ridicule, misinformation, and wild ideas, X rays almost immediately began to reach out to all the world. Four days from the time the news reached America, a doctor there used X rays to locate a bullet in the leg of a patient. Within six months of Roentgen's discovery, a scientist in Berlin was feeding lead compounds to guinea pigs and photographing their stomachs with X rays. Before 1896 ended, Dr. W. B. Cannon in America had substituted bismuth in this technique and was making X-ray pictures of the animals' organs. By 1898 this was applied to humans.

While scientists all over the world immediately began to use X rays and equipment suppliers and others got rich on the new technology, Roentgen himself never profited by a penny from his invention. Neither did Roentgen avail himself of the title of nobility that could have been his—a "Von" before his name. World War I ruined him financially, since he gave all his assets and even his gold medals to his country. After the war he lived frugally on a pension which forced him to "continually practice more and more economy," as he put it. Roentgen died on February 10, 1923.

Becquerel and radioactivity

Roentgen received the Rumford science medal in 1896, jointly with physicist Philipp Lenard. In 1901, Roentgen became the first physicist to receive a Nobel prize. In 1903 another man received the same award. Roentgen's award was for discovering artificial radiation; Antoine Becquerel dis-

Thomas Edison experimented briefly with X rays. This engraving from a French publication of 1896 shows him with his version of a fluoroscope. The black box contains the tube, which has been exhausted through the mercury vacuum pump shown on the upright board. A Ruhmkorff coil at the right supplied high voltage.

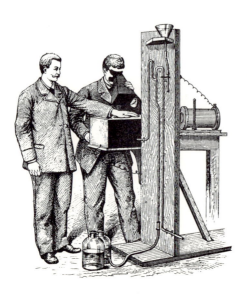

covered *natural* radiation—something we now call radio-activity, including gamma rays, which are more powerful than X rays.

Gamma rays are close cousins to X rays, but farther along in the electromagnetic spectrum and therefore shorter in wave-length, higher in frequency, and more energetic. Coinciden-tally, they were discovered just a year after X rays, and just as much by accident. The French physicist Antoine Henri Becquerel was interested, as his father had been, in the phenomenon of fluorescence. This was the glowing of cer-tain minerals when subjected to ultraviolet light. In this strange process, invisible radiation was converted somehow into visible light of a rather ghostly quality. Even today, the use of "black light" and fluorescent paint causes startling colors.

Becquerel stored his photographic plates near his collection of fluorescing minerals and one day he used a plate only to find it spoiled as if previously exposed. Investigating, he found that apparently some "pitchblende from Bohemia" from his rock collection was the culprit. This was in 1896, shortly after Roentgen's fortunate accident with the Crookes tube. After a similar period of feverish investigation, Becquerel realized he had discovered something similar: invisible rays able to penetrate paper and cardboard. The difference was that the Roentgen rays were artificially produced while Becquerel's were natural. In a letter to the French Academy of Sciences, Becquerel wrote:

I can only surmise that we are dealing with a new kind of radiation apparently related to that which M. Roentgen has discovered at Würzburg. How do I arrive at this view? Like this, the radiation penetrates opaque bodies, and darkens a photographic plate when all light is switched off. Indeed, even when the plates are enclosed in a lightproof container with only a small amount of air space between them and the source of radiation. It also turns the air surrounding it into a conductor of electricity. In other words, it manifests all the same characteristics as Roentgen's rays. Nevertheless, I cannot make up my mind to regard it as identical with these, for its place of origin is not a tube of Roentgen's design, but simply, as already stated, uranium salts.

Baron Ernest Rutherford, studying a tiny sample of radium later, would indeed find that it produced rays that were not identical with those of Roentgen's X-ray generator. The emitted radiation from the radium had an energy far greater than that produced by Roentgen's equipment.

Becquerel placed a magnet around the stream of rays from his radioactive uranium and found that part of the radiation was deflected toward one side and part toward the opposite side, indicating that some of the radiation consisted of positively charged particles and some of negatively charged particles. In 1899 Rutherford performed similar experiments and named the different particles alpha and beta. This same division of the energy stream can be accomplished with an electric field as well as a magnet; the beta rays, or electrons, bending toward the positively charged plate and the alpha rays, or positive helium nuclei, bending toward the negative one. A year after Rutherford's demonstration, P. Villard of France demonstrated yet a third type of radiation from uranium; this consisted of gamma rays, which had no elec-

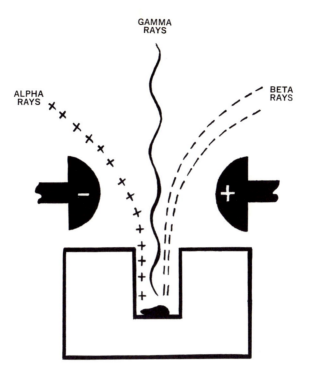

GAMMA RAYS

ALPHA RAYS

BETA RAYS

Radiation from radium or some other radioactive substance can be separated into alpha rays, beta rays, and gamma rays by means of charged plates, the positive plate attracting the negative beta rays, or electrons, and the negative plate attracting the positive alpha rays. Gamma rays, being energy waves and carrying no charge, proceed straight upward from the source. A magnet can be used to make such a separation also. The lead container absorbs all rays except those escaping out of the hole at the top.

trical charge at all and so shot straight forward without bending.

In 1903 Marie Curie presented her doctoral thesis, which included a diagram of the splitting of alpha, beta, and gamma rays in a magnetic field. This simple but important diagram is now the symbol of the Oak Ridge National Laboratory.

Radioactive rays, or Becquerel's rays, as they were called for some time, actually began the atomic age. Madame Curie carried on Becquerel's work and refined uranium to radium, a million times more active than its parent substance. Radio-active materials showed that matter could be converted to energy, and atom-smashers like Lord Rutherford duplicated the process artificially. Patrick M. S. Blackett did the opposite by allowing gamma rays to pass through a lead plate. Sometimes the rays disappeared, changed into a positron and an electron, two particles of matter where only energy had existed before.

4   penetrating radiation

The basic unit of light energy is the "photon." This word was invented by Arthur Holly Compton, an American physicist, in 1923. It is hard to picture a photon. Such a particle when standing still has no mass or inertia and would seem to be an imaginary concept. However, photons never stand still. As we shall see, they may possess tremendous energy, particularly in the range of X rays and gamma rays.

Electromagnetic waves are measurable in three respects. These are frequency, wavelength, and energy. Since all electromagnetic waves travel at the same speed, we can convert frequency to wavelength, or vice versa. Here is the basic formula:

$$F \times W = S,$$

or, frequency times wavelength equals the speed of light. If we know the wavelength, we divide the speed of light by it and get the frequency. Or, dividing the speed of light by the frequency, we find the wavelength. Furthermore, dividing the universal constant for radiant energy (worked out by physicist Max Planck) by the wavelength of radiation gives the quantum energy for that particular radiation.

In addition to their being measureable, electromagnetic waves have other characteristic properties. They may be reflected or bounced from a smooth surface, refracted or bent as Newton did light waves with his prism, and focused as in a telescope or burning glass. Although Roentgen reported failure in these respects for his rays, it was soon learned that X rays could be reflected and refracted under certain critical conditions.

It is said that dynamite comes in small packages, and the same idea is true of electromagnetic energy. First let's get an idea of the measurements of various kinds of electromagnetic radiation we have talked about. Waves generated in alternating current power lines are longer than 1,000 miles. Some radio broadcast waves are a mile long; television waves about one yard. Radar waves are much shorter, some of them being about an inch in length. This seems small but is far longer than the wavelength of visible light. The colors we see are caused by photons whose waves are short as bacteria, far less than one-thousandth of an inch. Ultraviolet waves are about one-millionth of an inch long. All of these are long, however, when compared to "hard" radiation: X rays are only a billionth of an inch long and gamma rays only a trillionth.

A wave that is long cannot also be strong. In fact, the energy of radiation is proportional in reverse order to size. While long radio waves do penetrate some materials—or we would not be able to enjoy our radios without an outside antenna—they slip through without really disturbing any-thing. Not so with hard radiation. X and gamma rays are veritable little giants. Packed with electrical energy, they are able to penetrate solid material and cause great damage to living cells. X rays and gamma rays are the fastest-vibrating radiation.

There are waves with a frequency of only one cycle per 100 seconds and a wavelength of 18,600,000 miles. The photons associated with these long-wave, very weak radiations have an energy barely detectable in electron volts (commonly abbreviated ev). Long radio waves, for example, have only 0.00000001 ev of energy. Microwaves, in the radar range right next to the infrared part of the spectrum, have a much higher frequency of vibration and a much shorter wavelength. They also have many times the energy and are rated at about 0.001 ev maximum. The strongest infrared waves, those near the red wavelength we can see, have about 1.5 ev. Visible light consists of photons with energies ranging from about 1.6 ev for red to 2.7 for violet. While these energies are incomparably higher than those of long radio waves, they are insignificant compared to those of X and gamma rays.

The strongest ultraviolet light—the kind that sunburns us strongly—ranges up to 100 ev. X rays pick up where the ultra-violet leaves off and go to 100,000 ev. Gamma rays go far higher than this, to several million. The radiation we are discussing in this book, then, is vastly more powerful than the strongest visible sunlight we are exposed to on earth. It is no surprise that it should be called "penetrating" radiation. Unlike alpha and beta particles, X rays and gamma rays do not have an electrical charge. This makes them even more penetrating, since—though to some extent they can knock electrons out of atoms—they do not "become involved" in a highly active way with the atoms they penetrate, as the positive alpha and negative beta particles do.

A sheet of paper will stop alpha rays emitted by radium; glass a half inch thick stops beta rays. However, gamma rays from the same source penetrate several inches of lead; in air strong gamma rays can travel for hundreds of feet. About four inches of water reduces the strength of gamma radiation of one million electron volts to half; eight inches of water to one-quarter, 12 inches to one-eighth. Thus gamma radiation penetrates deeply.

Electromagnetic radiation of a particular wavelength is identical with all other radiation of the same wavelength, regardless of the source of such radiation. For example, the spectrum of X rays overlaps that of gamma rays. Whether we call waves in this overlap X rays or gamma rays for convenience does nothing to change their nature. A photon with a wavelength of 1 angstrom is the same whether it is artificially produced as an X ray or naturally emitted as a gamma ray. It is simply a matter of definition: in general we may say that X rays are produced by bombarding atoms with electrons, while gamma rays are produced from within an atomic nucleus by radioactive processes. Roentgen and Becquerel were dealing with the same rays, produced in different ways.

Atoms are composed of a nucleus with a positive charge surrounded by electrons revolving around the nucleus in one or many "shells," or orbits, depending on the kind of atom we are dealing with. When only the electrons in the outer shell are disturbed by outside forces (such as a stream of electrons or a beam of light), visible light is given off. This is the familiar phenomenon of luminescence, as seen, for instance, in the firefly or in push buttons that glow in the dark. But if the electrons of inner shells are disturbed and jump to another shell, more energetic radiation results. An X-ray tube has sufficient energy to produce not visible radiation from target atoms, but X radiation. The higher the voltage of the cathode-ray stream, the higher the energy of the X rays until they approach gamma rays in strength.

When a cathode ray bombards a target, a shower of X rays of various wavelengths is produced. There are also X rays of a particular wavelength, characteristic of the target material, that are emitted. One analogy used to clarify the production of X rays is that of a marble striking a bass drum. Here we have a solid object creating a sound wave as the result of the collision. If an electron strikes a proper target atom—such as the glass of Roentgen's Crookes tube, or the tungsten target of a modern-day X-ray tube—electromagnetic waves are produced.

X rays are produced by the conversion of the kinetic energy (motion energy) of cathode rays into radiant energy. Gamma rays, on the other hand, are ejected from the disintegrating nuclei of the atoms of radioactive materials, either natural or man-made. In this kind of radiation, matter itself is being converted into energy. Atomic bomb fallout and other dangerous radiation from nuclear reactors is principally in the form of gamma rays, which are more energetic and penetrating than the alpha and beta rays also produced by nuclear sources.

x-ray sources

Roentgen's first X-ray tube was a makeshift, not even designed to do what it did. It sprayed radiation wildly and was most inefficient. But it worked. For such a tremendous scientific advance, it was inexpensive to purchase. An article in the *American Medical Journal* in 1896 referred to the fluoroscope as "Roentgen's Spectacles." The cost was about that of spectacles, too; prices ranged from five to twenty dollars.

Crookes tubes were generally pear-shaped glass affairs, produced by the glassblower's art. Imbedded in the tube were two electrodes, the cathode or negative side of an electrical circuit, and the anode or positive side. Air was pumped out of the tubes to make for easy passage of the stream of cathode rays from cathode to anode. Sometimes gas was introduced into the tube and then the problem was to maintain a steady amount of pressure as gas leaked away. One clever solution was to form a pocket in the tube to hold a substance which when heated would generate more gas to replace what was lost.

The basic operation of an X-ray tube. The older tubes merely had a negative charge on the cathode; modern ones supply electrons from a hot filament, and the charged cathode repels them toward the anode. The impact of the electrons on the positive anode throws off X rays at an angle.   *General Electric Company*

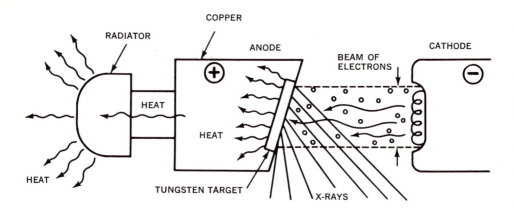

Slowly the design of X-ray tubes improved. The anode was placed directly across from the cathode so that rays would strike it instead of the glass. A "target" of the proper metal was placed on the anode and thus many more X rays were knocked out by the cathode rays streaming against it.

To provide electric current for firing the X-ray tube, Roentgen and others of his day used a crude spark generator. Only about 20,000 volts were produced and the beam of X rays was erratic and fluctuating. The equipment was noisy too.

One problem in early equipment was the production of heat. X-ray tubes are inefficient, more than 99 per cent of the energy being wasted in heat. This was why many early "roentgenologists" kept pails of water standing by in case of fire. Copper jackets were added to the tubes to carry heat away, and this helped somewhat.

In pioneer X-ray tubes the generator wires were attached to simple cathode and anode terminals. But with the knowledge that a heated cathode produced a cloud of electrons about it, W. D. Coolidge of the General Electric Company in 1912 added the "hot filament" to the cathode. Such an element, much like the glowing wire in a toaster, stimulated the flow of more electrons in the cathode-ray stream. This technique was similar to that used in the electronic tubes which become the heart of radio and other equipment. A small current applied to the filament or plate controlled a much larger current from cathode to anode.

The trouble with this improvement was that it increased the heating at the anode end of the tube. To lessen this problem, rotating anodes were developed. Turning at about 3,000 revolutions per minute, these allowed a different part of the metal target to be struck at any given time. One benefit of this improvement was the use of smaller targets, giving an X-ray beam of smaller proportions for more precise work.

Roentgen used direct current to energize his X-ray tubes. Today alternating current is more practical for medical and industrial X-ray equipment. This form of electricity, which varies rapidly from positive to negative and back again, must be converted into direct current by rectifiers. The clatter of early rectifiers has been silenced and today high-voltage X-ray generators are silent in operation, even up to millions of volts.

Today's X-ray tube consists of a cathode which beams electrons at a target set at an angle in the anode. Attached to the anode is a radiator to remove heat generated by the impact of electrons against the target. The angle of the target bounces X rays in the desired direction. The tube is usually of Pyrex glass, with as high a vacuum as it is possible to get.

X-ray equipment is available in a wide range of sizes, from small units for tooth X-raying to large treatment machines for cancer and other diseases. For treating skin disease, between 80,000 and 100,000 volts are normally applied to the tube. Stronger radiation, needing up to about 140,000 volts, treats inflammatory or infectious disease, and deep therapy for cancer requires about 200,000 volts.

Extremely high-voltage X rays are produced by the betatron. This doughnut-shaped vacuum tube is designed to accelerate electrons much faster than is possible in an ordinary X-ray tube. When the electrons are moving at the proper speed around and around in the tube, a magnet is switched on to make them change direction enough to strike a target as in the X-ray tube. X rays of tremendous energy—up to 23 million electron volts—are produced and fly out of the betatron. This radiation has been used to treat cancer. Linear ac-

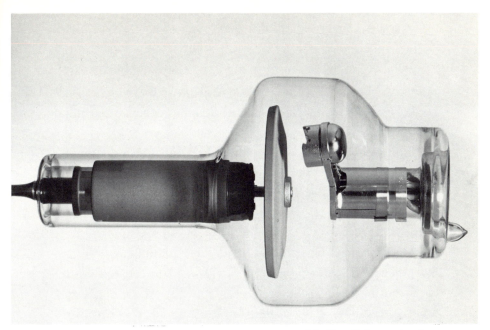

Machlett Laboratories, Inc.

A modern X-ray tube with a motor-driven rotating anode. As shown by contrasting the previous drawing with the one shown here, such an anode can give sharper details in the picture because it is possible for the focal spot—the point on the anode hit by the electrons—to be very small. A stationary focal spot of very small size would be burned away by the heat generated by the electron bombardment, but if the anode is rotated, the heat is distributed safely.

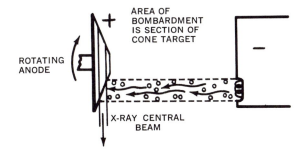

AREA OF
BOMBARDMENT
IS SECTION OF
CONE TARGET

ROTATING
ANODE

X-RAY CENTRAL
BEAM

General Electric Company

The rotating anode gives an X-ray beam that has narrower areas of blur in each part of it.

celerators, king-size X-ray generators of great length, are also used. One at the Stanford Medical School generates six million electron volts.

Fluorescent screens have improved too, giving much brighter pictures with less radiation. This safeguards the patient and especially the doctor, who is exposed to radiation continually. Radiologists still wear red goggles, however, to adapt their eyes to see better the glow of the screen.

Improvements have been made in photography too. Roentgen and other pioneers used glass plates coated with emulsion made for ordinary photography. By 1920, film was used, a cellulose base coated with an emulsion of silver chloride or silver bromide which darkens when struck by radiation. Dr. Michael Pupin discovered a method of greatly improving X-ray photography while at Columbia University. His idea combines the fluorescing screen and photographic film. The fluorescing material results in greater contrast and detail on the film with less radiation. New amplification techniques have resulted in fluoroscopy screens 300 times as bright as conventional ones. These may be viewed in daylight rather than the darkroom and work well for X-ray moving pictures.

gamma-ray equipment

A large modern X-ray machine produces more powerful radiation than all the radium in the world. It operates for only about one dollar an hour. However, there are times when it is more convenient to use a gamma-ray generator fed by a radioactive source. Gamma-ray sources include radium, uranium, cobalt, cesium, strontium, potassium 40, polonium, carbon 14, tritium, thorium, phosphorus, to name a few. There are more than 1,000 radioisotopes, of which 150 are sold commercially.

Since gamma rays are similar to X rays, they are used in many of the same ways. Radium treatments have long been given, but today cobalt therapy is most popular, using the radioisotope known as cobalt 60. Such equipment can provide radiation equivalent to that produced by three-million-volt electrical X-ray generators. Also, it doesn't require a power supply of high voltage as does X-ray equipment. The "cobalt bomb" is often used in the unusual technique of rotating it about the body of the patient with the area to be treated at the center of rotation. This gives a maximum of treatment at the desired point, yet, for relative safety, minimizes the radiation to other parts of the body.

Perhaps the largest gamma-ray emitter ever used is the 12,000-curie unit at Brookhaven. Contrasted to this are small portable units using thulium as a radioactive source and weighing but a few pounds.

5   x rays and science

It was not a medical doctor or industrial engineer who discovered X rays. Dr. Roentgen was a scientist. As Thomas Edison pointed out, Roentgen "belongs to those scientists who study for pleasure and love to delve into the secrets of nature." Happily, X rays have proved of tremendous value not only to medicine and industry but to science as well.

Roentgen discovered X rays in 1895. By 1912 the mysterious radiation was much used but still not fully understood. No one really knew what it was. Roentgen himself thought that X rays were probably "longitudinal vibrations in the ether." Others thought that X rays were particles like the cathode rays that produced them. Some maintained, however, that X rays were electromagnetic waves like light waves. In 1912 Max von Laue suggested that X rays could be diffracted, and this was soon confirmed by two of his associates. He also measured the wavelengths of X rays.

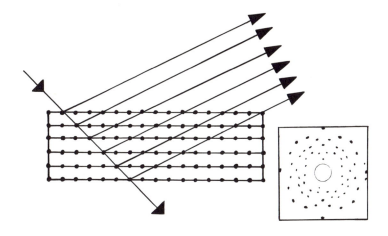

A crystal is made up of atoms arranged in regular planes equidistant from each other, and the atoms in each plane are also arranged at regular distances. This simplified diagram shows how the X rays, entering at left, are reflected from individual atoms. After bouncing out of the crystal, the X rays from different atomic planes overlap with a phase difference and produce spots on a film. The pattern of such a Laue photograph, of a rock salt crystal, is shown in the smaller drawing.

x-ray diffraction and spectroscopy

Laue knew that X rays were much shorter in wavelength than ordinary light and thus would be more difficult to diffract with a grating ruled on glass such as scientists used for visible light—if it was possible at all. But there existed in nature a much finer "diffraction grating." This was the atomic structure of a crystal, composed of an orderly row of atoms in a lattice-like structure. Zinc sulfide was selected by Laue as his X-ray diffraction grating, and it worked just as he hoped it would.

Beaming X rays at a slight angle to his crystal, Laue exposed a photographic plate. He developed it, and there on the emulsion was a pattern of the atomic structure of the crystal

63

as revealed by the wavelength of the X rays. Using the same frequency X rays to trace the atomic pattern of the crystal always resulted in the same telltale "picture" of the crystal. And using a known crystal always resulted in the same pattern for a given X ray. Science gained two tools as a result of Laue's experiment: it could identify crystals *or* X rays. From using crystals to check X radiation, science moved on to using the X rays to do scientific detective work on crystals. Several new elements have been identified by using this method.

Just as X rays permit a doctor to peer inside his patient and identify a disease or problem, X rays let the scientist look right inside tiny crystals or crystalline powders and identify a substance. And this is done with no harm to the material.

Shortly after Laue's work, Henry Moseley, an English physicist, developed X-ray spectroscopy, the identification of elements by the wavelengths of the X rays emitted when he bombarded them with electrons. Moseley was able to show that the atomic number of elements and their X-ray spectra were directly related. He suggested an improvement in the periodic tables of the Russian Dmitri Mendeleev and showed that there remained only seven missing elements between hydrogen and uranium.

The effectiveness of the X-ray spectroscopy technique was demonstrated when Moseley analyzed brass to show spectral lines of copper and zinc from it. This was the first use of his X-ray technique in chemical analysis.

x-ray microscopes

The electron microscope was invented because scientists realized that ordinary light microscopes were limited in their magnification power to about 3,000 diameters. This is so because of the length of light waves. When the size of an object to be magnified is about half the wavelength of the light used to study it, the light rays begin to bend around the tiny object and no longer accurately reflect its size and other factors. Electrons are far smaller than visible light waves and permit magnification of several hundred thousand times. However, there are limitations to the electron microscope too.

One disadvantage is that the electron microscope requires a vacuum and thus it is usually impossible to study living things with it. With an X-ray microscope living specimens could be studied. X rays are more penetrating too, and can be used to study thicker specimens than can electrons. And X rays, like electrons, have very short wavelengths, as much as 10,000 times shorter than light waves.

Although X rays exhibit all the properties of light waves, including reflection, refraction, focusing, and magnification, they do not have these properties in the same amount. For instance, reflection of X rays occurs only at very slight "grazing angles." An X ray beamed straight at a reflecting surface goes right through it. However, even with these limitations, X rays have been tamed sufficiently to make microscopes. In 1948 Dr. Paul Kirkpatrick of Stanford University built the first X-ray microscope. He found that gold mirrors of elliptical shape rather than spherical ones give best results. Magnification of up to 1,000 diameters has been achieved, and objects as small as 0.25 micron show clearly. A micron is 39 millionths of an inch.

The great beauty of X-ray microscopy is that it can penetrate solid specimens and give chemical as well as physical information. Accurate analyses can be made of samples weighing only one-hundred-trillionth of a gram. X-ray microscopy is used in inorganic and organic chemistry, metallurgy, mineralogy, and of course in biology. Microradiograms have been made of the finest blood vessels. It is even possible to make stereoscopic X-ray microscope pictures so they appear to have roundness and solidity.

x-ray absorptometry

Another scientific X-ray technique is called absorptometry, the accurate measurement of the amount of X radiation absorbed by various substances. The atoms of a given element always absorb the same amount of X radiation, whether the atom is alone or linked to other elements in a solid, liquid, or gaseous compound. This makes it possible to measure, for example, the amount of ethyl in gasoline. Absorptometery also makes possible the measurement of thickness of materials, or the counting of a number of thin sheets or films by passing X rays through them and measuring the amount of X rays absorbed in the process.

the Mössbauer effect

Just as there is resonance in sound (sympathetic vibration) and light (the fluorescence Becquerel was studying when he discovered radioactivity), it can be achieved with gamma rays also. A young German physicist, Rudolf Mössbauer, in 1959 succeeded in producing the gamma-ray resonance which now bears his name. With the target nuclei at rest, the emitted gamma rays would be exactly the frequency of those striking the target. But any movement of the target, however slight,

The beautiful inner structure of these marine snail shells is revealed by X rays.

puts the two radiations out of phase. Ordinarily the nuclei in the atoms of a substance—especially a gas—recoil, as a gun recoils when it is shot off, when gamma rays hit them. Mössbauer overcame this by using a crystal as the target; there was no observable distortion, because the recoil was distributed over the very many nuclei in the crystal.

Thus the Mössbauer effect can be used as a very accurate clock or measuring device. In 1960 two physicists at Harvard University put it to work to determine if gravity had the effect of shortening the wavelength of gamma radiation, as Einstein had predicted. Beaming gamma rays of one wavelength downward a distance of 75 feet, they proved that the wavelength was indeed shortened. Gravity increased the energy of the gamma rays.

x rays in natural science

X rays are important in natural science as well as physical science. Naturalists can study the fossil remains of life forms and learn much. For example, the diseases suffered by prehistoric men and animals are studied by X-raying the fossil remains. Mummies can be studied by X rays without destroying tissues.

Evolution studies profit from X rays. Such photographs of the remains of a crocodile of 200 million years ago disclosed details of tooth development not suspected before.

It has been suggested that fossils be located in blocks of soil or rock by X-ray photography. One particularly interesting use of X rays on fossils proved that the Piltdown skull was a fraud. Gypsum was discovered by X-ray diffraction studies of the jaw and canine tooth; the same material also was found

68

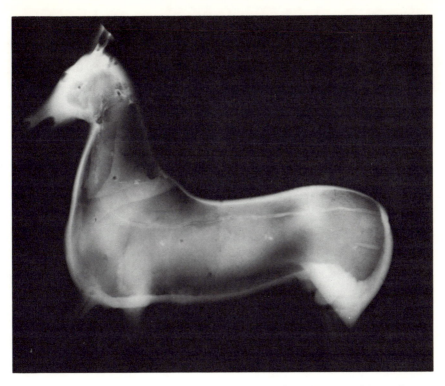

Gamma as well as X rays help detect art frauds. This bronze statuette of a horse was on exhibit for years as an apparently genuine ancient Greek piece of art dating from about 470 B.C. In 1967 this gamma-ray shadowgraph, using iridium 192, showed the internal sand-core structure to be supported by iron wires (seen principally as a long streak from the tail up into the head). This is a completely modern method of construction.

in Neolithic bones. This proved that the claimed archaeological find was actually a faked Neolithic skull. Similar fraud detection by X rays has been done in the art field, the most recent and dramatic being of the Van Meegeren fraudulent painting attributed to the famous Dutch painter Vermeer.

The development of eggs may be studied nondestructively with X rays, and botanists use them to trace the structure of leaves. Fish are X-rayed in various ways and in the case of

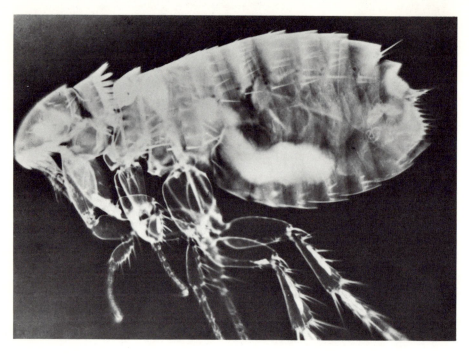

The common flea that attacks man, *Pulex irritans*, as seen by X rays.

rare fishes, valuable information comes from learning the contents of their stomachs in this way without dissecting them. X rays revealed that the wax in the ears of whales has a new layer for each two-year period, so now it is possible to determine a whale's age by a method somewhat like the growth-ring technique used with trees.

x-ray astronomy

Astronomers learned things astronomical primarily by observing the celestial objects. That is, they used the visible light coming from these bodies. True, in some cases the attraction of gravity, something we cannot see, was used to great advan-

70

tage in working out some of the problems of celestial mechanics. But visible light provided most of the information for astronomy.

Science often works in a roundabout way. Helium, for instance, was discovered not on earth but in the sun as an unidentified spectral line. To find X rays, which are produced in quantity by our sun, Roentgen had to stumble onto man-made radiation in his laboratory. And to use natural X rays in astronomy took about half a century from the time the first X rays were recognized in Germany.

Astronomers did not jump from optical waves directly to X rays. Radio waves were the first of the invisible waves used to expand knowledge of the sky. Thomas Edison suggested in 1890 that radio waves might be received from the sun. The English scientist Sir Oliver Lodge tried to detect them as early as 1897 but failed. Success had to wait until long after Marconi built the first radio. From America to England to Italy the chain of progress passed again to America.

Karl G. Jansky was a young radio engineer working in 1932 at Bell Telephone Laboratories on the problem of static that hampered radio reception. One source of these radio discharges could not be traced to any man-made or atmospheric disturbance, and Jansky finally reached the remarkable conclusion that they must be coming from outer space. By 1933 Jansky was sure that the strange radio waves were coming from the plane of the Milky Way—especially from Sagittarius and several other constellations. This is near the center of our galaxy. It happened that Jansky did his first work when sunspot activity of the sun was at a low, and its radio outpourings did not override those from farther out in space.

Astronomers used to their familiar optical telescopes did not immediately take to the new kind of star-probing. In fact, the only person who carried on Jansky's work was a young man named Grote Reber. Reber was a "ham" and for his own satisfaction he spent much time in his backyard radio shack in Wheaton, Illinois, investigating the strange waves from space. Since these waves were far longer than light waves, a radio telescope required a much larger reflector than an optical telescope. Reber built a dish-shaped antenna 30 feet in diameter with which he scooped up incoming radiation. He began his experiments in 1938 but World War II soon intervened.

British radar scientists noted that radio signals in the microwave or radar region were reaching earth from the sun. Particularly was this so when sunspot activity was high, and in 1942 a solar flare drowned out the radar networks in England. After the war British scientists built the huge 250-foot radio telescope at Jodrell Bank, still used in astronomy and also space communications. Since then radio telescopes several times as large as the Jodrell Bank giant have been built. The biggest is at Arecibo, Puerto Rico and is 1,000 feet in diameter.

Closer to home than the sun, radio emissions were received from the moon and planets. But the most valuable to astronomers were waves ranging from 0.3 centimeter to 30 meters. These pass through a "window" in our atmosphere, but other radio waves of shorter and longer wavelengths are stopped. Very short waves are absorbed in the air, and longer waves are bounced off the ionospheric layer surrounding the earth.

Radio telescopes turned up hitherto unknown stars.

Astronomer Walter Baade used radio astronomy to find two galaxies in the process of colliding, some 260 million light years away. And by tuning in on the radio broadcast of hydrogen atoms colliding in space (a wavelength of 21 centimeters) astronomers have traced the huge spiral arms of our own galaxy, undetectable in any other way.

Radio astronomy has some great advantages over optical methods. Atmospheric disturbances do not affect reception, nor do clouds of dust in space. Perhaps the greatest advantage, however, lies in the fact that radio telescopes reach out much farther than do optical telescopes. Celestial objects have been located first by radio and only then spotted in the conventional way. Some of these have never been seen, either because they are too distant for light waves to reach or perhaps emit no visible light waves.

Strong sources of radio waves in the Milky Way are the supernovas or particularly bright exploded stars. Examples are the Crab Nebula, and the supernovas recorded in 1572 and 1604. Cassiopeia A, discovered first by radio and then faintly seen at a distance of about 10,000 light-years with the 200-inch Palomar telescope, is also thought to be the remains of a supernova which exploded about 1702.

Oddly, some radio signals did not seem to be associated with visible stars, or are some distance from the nearest visible celestial objects. Most interesting of the radio stars are the quasars, or quasi-stellar radio sources. Over 100 of these have been discovered. They seem to be rushing away from us at fantastic speeds. The farthest yet recorded by radio waves is the quasar 3C 147, estimated to be 4,000 million light-years distant.

Astronomy now used not only optical telescopes but radio

telescopes as well and had broadened the range of its "vision" to include much of the radio spectrum as well as the infrared, visible light, and ultraviolet. What of the wavelengths just shorter than the ultraviolet—the X rays man had known about for half a century? These too are absorbed in our protective envelope of atmosphere and so are not detected at the earth's surface. X-ray astronomy had to wait for the age of space so that suitable "telescopes" could rise into the vacuum of outer space.

Scientists first knew only in 1949 that our sun produces X rays. In that year a V-2 rocket fired from White Sands, New Mexico, brought back proof that such radiation was present 100 miles above the earth. Dr. Herbert Friedman pioneered this research and today continues to do X-ray astronomy for the Naval Research Laboratory.

The production by our sun of X rays is rather surprising, since its surface temperature of 6,000 degrees is too low to do the job. It seems that the sun's corona—a thin outer layer of gases—must be radiating the X rays, since when solar flares (sudden bright eruptions) occur, the X radiation received on earth increases greatly.

In 1962 a rocket carrying instruments for detection of fluorescence X radiation from the moon was lofted 130 miles into the air. Although Geiger counters measured such radiation during the trip, it was found when the data were analyzed that the radiation was not fluorescent and not from the moon. Instead, like Jansky's radio waves, it came generally from the center of our galaxy and was background X radiation. There was a lesser amount coming from the general direction of the strong radio stars Cassiopeia A and Cygnus A. X-ray astronomy was established.

In 1963 Friedman and other researchers launched a rocket with X-ray detectors some ten times as sensitive as those used in earlier attempts. Results showed two sources of X rays in the heavens. One very strong one was in the constellation Scorpius; the other, much weaker, apparently came from the Crab Nebula. The Crab Nebula of course had been located visually and by radio telescope but the Scorpius X-ray source had not been detected in either way. It was suggested that what Friedman and his colleagues had found was a "neutron star." Following the discovery of Scorpio XR-1, as Friedman named the X-ray star, a visible star of the thirteenth magnitude was located. Such a brightness is about what the scientist expected for the neutron star.

Astronomers Walter Baade and Fritz Zwicky had first proposed the neutron star in 1934, about the time Karl Jansky was first poking about the heavens with radio telescopes. A neutron star would be formed, if Baade and Zwicky were correct, by the collapse of a supernova into a dense core made up almost entirely of neutrons. Such a neutron star would be only about ten miles in diameter but would have about the mass of our sun. With an internal temperature of a few billion degrees and a surface at 10 million degrees Kelvin, the neutron star would radiate nearly all its energy as X rays rather than as visible light. In fact, the X radiation would exceed the visible light by some 10 billion times.

Thinking that the weaker emission from the Crab Nebula might also be from a neutron star, Friedman fired another rocket in 1964, just as the moon passed between Earth and the Crab Nebula. He felt that if the source really was a neutron star, the X-ray emission should stop abruptly as the moon occulted, or blocked out, the nebula. Instead, the

76

emission waned slowly. Analysis showed that the source was about one light year across and apparently not a neutron star. The possibility that the Scorpius source may be a neutron star is still being investigated. It is interesting that astronomical history in the Orient lists four events in the general area of Scorpius that may have been supernovas.

In 1965 scientists did additional theoretical work on the idea of neutron stars and decided that if such stars were indeed born they would cool very quickly—perhaps in a matter of weeks—and stops radiating X rays. Thus, finding a neutron star would be a most difficult feat, since it is impossible to keep a close X-ray watch on the events of the heavens all the time.

In 1967 an instrumented Aerobee rocket launched from White Sands detected X-ray emissions from the quasar 3C-273-B, thought to be about one-sixth of the distance from Earth to the edge of the universe. This was the first known X-ray reception from a quasar. It was also found that M-87, a cluster of stars in the constellation Virgo, emits X rays. This

M87, a cluster of some thousand million stars in the constellation Virgo, was the first object outside our galaxy identified as an emitter of X rays.　　　　　　　　　　　　　*U. S. Naval Observatory* was the first known X-ray reception from outside our galaxy. Three additional X-ray sources were located, none of them known quasars or radio galaxies.

Professor K. G. McCracken of the University of Adelaide and Dr. A. G. Fenton of the University of Tasmania launched Skylark rockets from the Woomera test range in Australia in April 1967, and reported an X-ray source. Their own further observations, and those of American scientists, of the same source seemed to indicate a drastic reduction in the amount of X-ray radiation being received. In a period of three weeks the source lost 30 per cent of its energy, and in another seven weeks had dropped considerably more. Along with the decrease in amount of X-ray radiation was a softening of the radiation—a shift to longer-wavelength X rays. These indications suggested that the star causing the X-ray emanations may have a total life of only two years or so.

While the search of the heavens beyond our solar system went on, other researchers continued to seek X rays from the planets. However, just as none were detected from our moon, none were found in balloon-borne detector studies of Mars, Venus, and Jupiter late in 1967. Although it was not expected that X rays would be found on Mars or Venus, there had been hope that Jupiter would yield some. It was suggested following their negative results that more sensitive detectors might eventually turn up the sought-for radiation.

Friedman's X-ray "telescope" is a four-square-foot panel of honeycomb-like metal strips. Although X rays are much more energetic than radio waves, those detected in space by Friedman's research are much weaker than the man-made X rays used in medical and industrial applications. However, by increasing his X-ray "antenna" 100 times in area Friedman expects to make it 1,000 times more sensitive and thus detect sources far beyond its former reach.

gamma-ray astronomy

While X-ray astronomy proceeds quite successfully, a similar application using gamma rays is not doing as well. The well-known cosmic rays from space, whose research Dr. Robert Millikan pioneered, consist partly of protons and other highly charged particles and partly of gamma rays.* These gamma rays are highly energetic. They have more energy than cosmic X rays, even more than most man-made X rays. A gamma-ray telescope is more complicated than an optical lens or mirror, or the Geiger counters of X-ray work. It consists of a spark chamber, bubble chamber, or cloud chamber, or a nuclear emulsion to track the fleeting gamma particles.

The first attempt to detect gamma rays from space took place in 1957. Thomas Cline sent a balloon to 110,000 feet, equipped with a gamma-ray "telescope." No gamma sources were detected, however. In 1958 two scientists at Massachusetts Institute of Technology, Drs. William L. Kraushaar and George W. Clark, began work on a gamma-ray detector for use in an orbiting satellite. They used a scintillation counter and another instrument called a Čerenkov counter. The complicated device was ready in 1961.

In that year the satellite Explorer XI was equipped with the gamma-ray telescope in an attempt to record gamma rays

---

* There is still some vagueness in the use of the term "cosmic rays." For instance, some authors, in describing the electromagnetic spectrum, include the cosmic rays as part of it, because of the gamma rays included in them; these gamma rays have an even higher frequency than gamma from ordinary sources. Others omit cosmic rays from the spectrum, because they consist *mainly* of particles rather than waves.

in space. The instrument did register impacts of 22 photons of gamma rays during four months of orbiting at from 300 to 1,100 miles high. These came from various directions and were believed to originate in intergalactic space. The Explorer research was not conclusive. Much more exciting was the announcement in 1966 by University of Rochester scientists that they had discovered a point source of gamma rays in Cygnus which they named GR-1. Further study indicated that the results were not entirely reliable, however.

Since gamma rays are not charged, they travel in straight lines through space and are not made to swerve by magnetic fields. This makes them important indicators for astronomers. However, it seems that gamma-ray strikes of Earth are relatively few. Biggest source of the radiation from deep space would be supernovas. These do not occur often, in fact only about once a century per galaxy. It is to be hoped that these problems will be surmounted and that gamma-ray astronomy will make contributions as important as those of X-ray star tracking.

6   radiation for sick bodies and faulty machines

Although Roentgen named his mysterious radiation X rays because of their unknown quality, little time was wasted in putting them to use. Scientists didn't know for sure what X rays were, but they did know how to use them. For example, on January 17, 1896, Dr. Sigmund Exner of Vienna exhibited X-ray pictures he had taken of the crooked healing of a fracture of a patient's finger struck by a bullet. Exner also showed what were probably the first angiographs, X rays of blood vessels injected with a dye that showed in the picture.

Within a week of Roentgen's first lecture at Würzburg an American doctor had used X rays to treat a skin condition in one of his patients. Another was using X rays to investigate the digestive tracts and other internal parts of animals. Surgeons used the strange penetrating rays to find "bullets, bones, and kidney stones" in human patients. Dr. Nicholas

Senn was trying to treat leukemia with X rays in Chicago
by 1903. Medical use of X rays, then, was the first application.

diagnosis by "looking in"

There are two ways in which doctors use X rays. First and
most obvious is to see into people. Broken bones can be
studied almost as easily as if the doctor were working with
a skeleton. The lungs, stomach, and other internal organs
can also be studied usefully.

Roentgen first noticed the X-ray effect on a sheet of treated
paper that fluoresced when struck by radiation. This technique
was adapted to make the fluoroscope, a screen on which the
doctor can see a patient's internal organs in action. Most of
us have had chest X rays. These simple and safe tests disclose
tuberculosis soon enough for its arrest and cure. Practical
jokers sometimes confuse the X-ray picture by taping a piece
of foil with the letters TB across their chests. This of course
can hide a telltale spot that might save their lives.

Air shows up on the film; this permits the taking of chest
X rays. Other materials can be used to outline other organs.
Almost as soon as Roentgen announced his discovery, a
German doctor fed lead compounds to guinea pigs and took
X-ray photographs of their stomachs. Later a similar technique
was used with humans and the taking of barium drinks
became commonplace. This harmless substance can be followed accurately down the digestive tract by the fluoroscope.
It shows up obstructions, foreign objects, and special conditions that may contribute to the ill health of a patient. To
make the barium drink better-tasting it is often flavored with
chocolate. Some doctors simply give the patient a carbonated

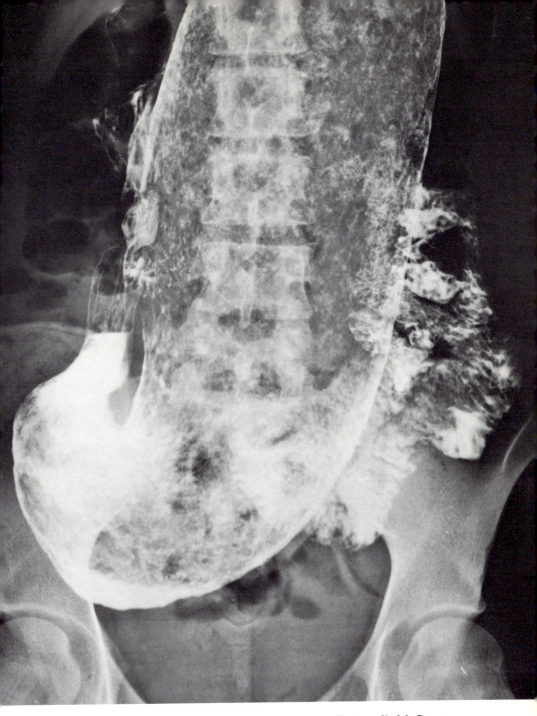

A large hair bulb in a human stomach, as shown by X rays. Under certain circumstances some persons become addicted to eating hair; this interferes with normal digestion.

drink, and in this case the bubbles show on the screen. Air bubbles injected into the brain are used to X-ray that delicate organ. Radiologists inject iodine for X-ray studies of lymph vessels, and iodized oil for the bronchial tree, or branching air tubes, in lungs.

To improve the quality and accuracy of X-ray pictures, a lead grid called a Potter Bucky diaphragm is slowly moved across the film during the exposure. This allows only direct X rays to penetrate the film and absorbs "secondary radiation" caused when primary rays strike the patient's body and bounce in various directions. If you've had chest X rays you will remember its slow sweep while you held your breath and tried to stay still for a good picture.

It was found that in treating disease deep in the body, inflammation of the skin by "soft" X rays hampered the treatment. Dr. George E. Pfahler pioneered the use of filters, experimenting first with leather—since it was approximately the density of human skin. Later he used aluminum, copper, and other metals. This technique proved very effective and gave relief deep in the body without harming the skin that intervened.

Many refinements have taken place in X-ray technique. For example, stereoscopic pictures give a three-dimensional effect that is invaluable to the surgeon preparing to operate. Color X-ray photography is possible by indirect means and this "color coding" adds another tool for diagnosis. An electronics firm has demonstrated an X-ray moving picture camera that enlarges the image three times. The goal of this work is to provide almost instantaneous, enlarged pictures for the surgeon as he works.

We have been discussing X-ray diagnosis in which a beam

of radiation is sent out from the generator, passes through the body, and thus makes a picture on film or fluoroscope screen. There is another method, in which radioisotopes—special radioactive forms of elements—are used. These are placed *inside* the patient; radiation for the diagnosis originates within instead of without. A variety of isotopes are used, depending on the disease. There is still much to be learned about them —particularly about the danger of cancer or other diseases developing much later from overirradiation with them.

Among the diagnostic isotopes is iodine 131, the "atomic cocktail" given to thyroid gland and brain tumor sufferers. Radiation from the iodine is traced in the patient by means of a Geiger counter and permits the doctor to tell whether

Strontium 90 on the tip of this needle is used to destroy nerve fibers in a spinal cord, to block pain. X rays make it possible to guide the needle with the necessary accuracy.

U. S. Atomic Energy Commission

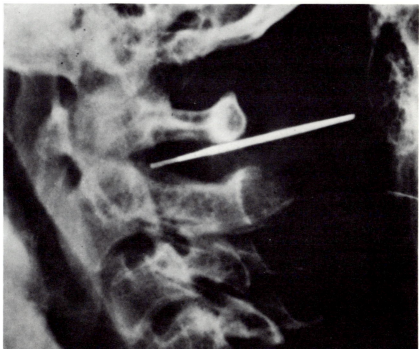

the thyroid is under- or overactive, or where the tumor is located. Gold radioisotopes concentrate in the liver; chromium 51 in red blood cells; phosphorus 32, barium 140, calcium 45, carbon 14, plutonium 239, radium 226, strontium 90, and uranium 233 are deposited in bone. Cesium 137 seeks muscle, cobalt 60 and polonium 210 the spleen.

Radioisotopes given to patients in a variety of ways perform both as picture-taking devices and as treatment for disease. The isotope gold 198 is an example. Pellets of radioactive gold are injected into cancerous cells. Tantalum 182, in the form of wire, is bent to desired shapes and used in cancer treatment.

Not only do the doctor and surgeon use X rays, but the dentist as well. Tooth X rays are a standard part of a dental examination and result in safer and better extractions and other tooth work. At the other end of our bodies, X rays were once widely used in shoe fitting. This application showed the customer his foot inside the new purchase, even letting him see the wiggle of his toes. However, this practice has waned because of the danger of too much radiation exposure; fortunately, it is gradually being made illegal. A shoe clerk is not a radiologist, and for several other reasons there is a strong probability of danger to customers and clerks. In Michigan some years ago, 51 per cent of the machines tested had too strong a beam, 50 per cent scattered radiation over people nearby, and 61 per cent had unsafe timing devices. Two leading experts on radiation, Dr. Jack Schubert and Dr. Ralph Lapp, have said that the use of X rays for shoe fitting "cannot be condemned too strongly."

But when used with knowledge and care, X-ray photography and fluoroscopy permit very helpful studies of broken

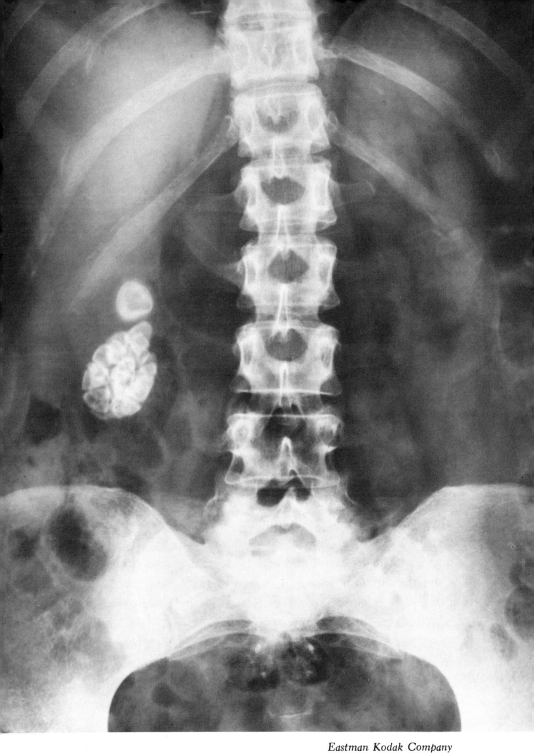

A group of gallstones shown in the human body by X rays. The stones, which are solid masses of mineral salts that can form in ducts and hollow organs, are seen at the middle, to the left of the spine. Notice also how the radiation shows up the relation between the vertebrae in the spine.

bones, internal organs, cancer, foreign objects, unborn children, and so on. X-ray diagnosis is a potent tool of modern-day medicine and many of us owe our lives to it.

x-ray therapy

There is a humorous story about a woman who was asked how her chest X ray went. "Wonderful," was her reply. "It felt so good I'm going right back down and have another!" While in this case there was confusion about the purpose of the test, X rays are used not only in diagnosis but treatment as well.

We have learned that X radiation is ionizing radiation, that it affects living cells by altering their atoms and molecules. Early users were unaware of this fact, and since X rays can't be seen or felt it was thought that they were as harmless as visible light. As a result, a number of doctors as well as patients suffered from X-ray burns. Because early X-ray machines were as inefficient as they were hot and noisy, a chest X ray might take as long as ten minutes and one of the hip or pelvis as long as 20 minutes. Also, the doctor might test his machine to find if it was warmed up by putting his own hand in the beam and making several test pictures.

In the Spanish-American war, the first in which X-ray diagnosis was used, a soldier named Thomas McKenna received severe burns on his arm and chest from three X-ray exposures, none of which produced a satisfactory picture of the gunshot wound to his right arm. The painful ulcers took almost a year to heal. Such things occurred repeatedly in the earlier years of the technique. However, it was the doctors themselves who suffered most, since they were exposed to

88

radiation not just once or a few times but constantly. Even today it is thought that radiologists, who are trained in careful use of equipment and well protected, live five years less on the average than other doctors. A large number of them suffer and die from leukemia, cancer, and other diseases aggravated by X rays.

Nevertheless, though the radiation causes everything from the loss of hair and fingernails to burns and death, it can also be used beneficially. Soft X rays are used on skin diseases and the treatment of carbuncles and similar eruptions. X-ray therapy is used on bursitis, an inflammation in the joints. In such cases there is increasing doubt, however, as to the wisdom of adding to the body's burden of accumulated radiation for diseases that are less than desperate. Hard X rays are used to treat cancer with some success. Sometimes X-ray treatment is combined with surgery, sometimes the X rays alone do the job. In one technique the patient (or ray machine) is rotated, with the ailing area at the center of rotation. Since it alone will receive the large dose of X rays, it is possible to give massive doses of radiation to a tiny area without harm to the rest of the body.

An important forward step in X-ray treatment was the establishment of safe amounts of radiation. Early researchers worked by guess, and without standard equipment it was impossible to specify proper doses and times of treatment. However, modern equipment, proper shielding, and knowledge of the effect of radiation on cells is resulting in more careful scientific control of treatment. There is still much to be done in this area, however—especially in following up cases years later to see if any damage resulted.

We live in a world of natural radiation, with a background

level that is measurable. Some radiation seems beneficial; it may even be necessary to living things that have evolved in its environment. Man is learning how to use the stronger and seemingly deadly radiation of X rays—and even the more powerful gamma radiation of other sources—to kill disease and prolong life.

The importance of X rays in medicine is indicated in the fact that there are approximately a quarter of a million machines in use in the United States, with more than 20,000 of these in New York City alone. An estimated 150 million medical X rays, plus another 100 million tooth X rays, are given each year.

There are about 7,000 radiologists in the United States. These are medical doctors with full training in radiation techniques. Assisting the radiologists are some 70,000 technicians, or technologists, about three-fourths of them women. These specialists, many of whom hold college degrees in their field, prepare the X-ray opaque materials, make the patient ready for photography or fluoroscopy, and see to protective screening to guard against unnecessary exposure of the patient. Some 25 per cent of these technicians work in hospitals. The remainder are employed in doctor's offices, laboratories, clinics, health agencies, and schools.

For training technicians there are now "X-ray dummies" to be photographed or fluoroscoped. With a skeleton, and rubber or plastic "organs" and blood vessels, the artificial stand-in produces realistic X rays and avoids the danger of exposure to students "posing" for each other in X-ray practice. Opaque fluids can be introduced into the dummy, and its limbs and head are hinged for realistic movement. The device is manufactured by a pioneer X-ray equipment manufacturer.

industrial uses of x rays

Roentgen first detected X rays by their passage through materials other than human tissue. Wood and metal were tried, as in the photographs showing a row of weights within their wooden box.

Among collectors' items are bottles and other glass items that have long been exposed to sunlight and acquired a beautiful violet hue. This is the result of continual bombardment by the ultraviolet part of the spectrum. Early X-ray tubes that survive as museum pieces today often demonstrate this coloring, from a pale violet to purple, because of the passage of X rays through them. Some special commercial glasses produced today are purposely irradiated with X rays and other radiation.

It is not surprising that X rays are now used to check not only the human frame but many industrial items as well. We stake our lives on a number of metal objects, including airplane propellers, ship hulls, railroad tracks, tanks under pressure, and so on. Unfortunately we cannot see inside such objects. At one time such defects were detected only when there was a failure, often with tragic results. Bridge girders might give way, a rapidly rotating part fly to pieces, or some other violent failure occur. Unable to peer inside a thick metal structure, engineers could only cut it open to find hidden flaws. It was some consolation to saw a metal casting apart and find that it contained no airholes, cracks, or other weak spots, but naturally it was then a useless part, and who could be sure that the next one off the production line was sound? What was needed was a *nondestructive* testing method. It came with X-ray photography.

Westinghouse Electric Corporation

A portable X-ray apparatus can do many important testing jobs in factories. The tube, enclosed in a metal case, is so mounted on arms, pivots, and wheels that it can shoot X rays in any chosen direction. Control box is at left. The unit at right is a transformer that provides high voltage for the cathode, which it enters through the thick cable.

A new kind of inspector began to be seen in factories, armed with X-ray instruments that peered into castings and beams, that checked parts for aircraft, ships, autos, dams, and bridges. An X-ray photo might show an air bubble that made a part useless; it might show a crack that could be repaired. By the time the great Hoover Dam was built, X-ray photography permitted the testing of some 75 *miles* of welds in that huge structure. And the testing did nothing harmful to the welds.

Among the many things that can be tested by industrial X-raying are engine parts, gun barrels, ball bearings, radio tubes, coal, rubber tires, golf balls, glass, bakelite, wood, porcelain, eggs, and so on. When a university student was killed by a defective fencing foil, all these weapons were examined by X ray. A number were found similarly defective and disposed of.

We hardly expect to find logs being run through an X-ray chamber but that is exactly what a Swedish woodworking firm is doing. Using a computer to calculate the best way to cut up incoming logs is an improvement over older rule-of-eye methods. But addition of the X-ray eye in the chamber spots hidden knots and other flaws in the timber. In a mill where close to 4,000 logs are handled per hour as they move along a conveyor at a speed of 200 feet a minute, the X-ray method has proved 85 per cent accurate, compared with only 55 per cent for the older "eyeball" method.

An unusual use of gamma-ray spectrometry is being exploited in England, where airborne equipment is locating deposits of radioactive materials. Flying at about 500 feet, the sodium iodide scintillators have proved their ability to ferret out weak deposits of thorium, potassium, and uranium. The United Nations is carrying out a three-year study of Madras State in India, using this kind of equipment to locate radioactive material.

With a record of success in aircraft, it is possible that artificially produced X rays may be used on the moon to guide spacecraft to a soft landing with human crews aboard. The National Aeronautics and Space Administration in 1966 contracted with private agencies for research into development of X-ray altimeters for such use. The advantage of X rays over radar or visible light include the ability to pierce the flame of the retrorocket exhaust. This inferno blankets out normal radio waves, as has been evidenced in a number of manned orbital flights heard by many of us. X rays also penetrate the walls of a space ship with no difficulty.

The Air Force too is interested in X-ray altimeters and detection systems. As a navigation device, the X-ray altimeter would pierce all kinds of weather. For detection, it would locate camouflaged emplacements and have the further advantage of being very difficult to detect by the enemy.

In contrast to large industrial X-ray equipment are tiny tubes designed for testing of weapons, the tubes of which are only half an inch in diameter and 1½ inches long. This tiny tube uses a voltage of 30,000 volts, the voltage of Roentgen's much larger pioneer X-ray tubes. Another development is the

Manufactured products such as this pistol can be inspected rapidly for defects by looking through them with X rays.

Eastman Kodak Company

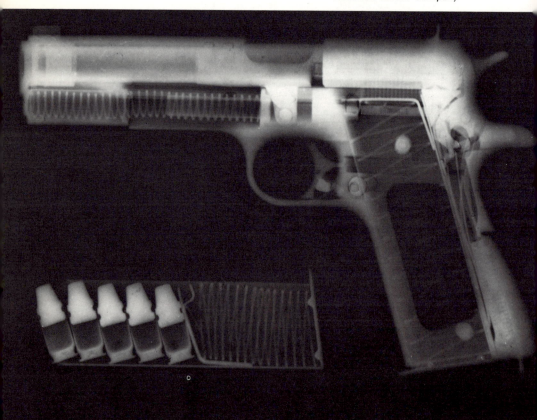

portable flash X-ray photography unit, comparable to the flash camera in conventional photography. Using a high-voltage pulse generator, the new equipment permits ultrahigh-speed X-ray photography.

Radiation gauges of many kinds are used widely in industry. The thickness of paper, metals, rubber, leather, adhesives, plastics, etc., are controlled by X rays and gamma rays. Other such equipment inspects bottles and cans on assembly lines for proper filling. Wear tests of rubber, metals, and other materials are made by coating them with radioactive material and monitoring them with X-ray equipment. In another application potassium 40 is used to provide gamma radiation in checking for foreign materials in wool.

radiation processing

In the next chapter we shall see that X rays and gamma rays have a drastic effect on living cells. Radiation can also change the chemical structure of nonliving materials. Early X-ray tubes were darkened by the passage of radiation through them. Plastics are affected too, as are transistors, rubber, oil, metals, organic liquids, and ceramics, to name a few. Uncontrolled irradiation is generally harmful, as in the damage to nuclear reactors subjected to long exposure to strong radiation. However, it has been learned that X rays and gamma rays can be used beneficially in some industrial processes.

Penetrating radiation produces "free radicals" (atoms or atom groups with at least one unpaired electron) in molecules and actually changes the chemistry of a material. It can bring about special kinds of polymerization (the building of large molecules from small ones), such as cross-linked and stable polymers. X rays and gamma rays act as catalysts to produce chemical structures unproducible in any other way. Some examples of what is called "process radiation" are the production of ethyl bromide, polyethylene film, cross-linked polyethylene wire, semiconductor products, plastics, rubber, and oil.

7 biological effects of x rays

It is well known that some animals can hear higher-pitched sounds better than others, and that some humans have ears that are more sensitive to certain ranges of notes than other people's. Young people generally hear higher-pitched sounds than their elders. During World War II it was learned that some pilots could see in the dark much better than others. Bees and other insects, and some crustaceans, can see polarized light. And human beings who have had operations that made it necessary to take out their eye lenses can thereafter usually see the ultraviolet part of the spectrum. There are more sensitivities than we might think.

But what of X rays? Even though they can destroy our eyes, we cannot see them. While we can see light waves and feel infrared, there seems no way of naturally detecting X rays. Actually, this is not really true, for it has been learned that cats and rats are able to accomplish this. Not by sight or

Case Institute of Technology

Somewhere in this rat's head are tissues that respond to X rays.

touch, but apparently by smell—or at least something connected with their olfactory, or smelling, organs. Sleeping rats awaken within two seconds after X rays are beamed at their noses, and they can be trained to perform certain tasks by the experimenters' using X rays as a biological signal.

Two theories have been advanced to account for this. One says that the rats detect the X rays not as smell but that the olfactory bulbs in their brains register them as a direct electromagnetic signal. The other argument offered is that it is not X rays that are smelled but the ozone produced in air by them. Interestingly, the Curies noted that radiation partially transformed oxygen to ozone, detectable by its pungent smell. However, further testing showed that detection does not depend on smelling ozone.

Moths of various species are sensitive to X rays of low intensity—"remarkably" so, according to the experimenters. In tests by James C. Smith and his colleagues, moths consistently started beating their wings whenever they were subjected to exposures as low as 0.01 roentgen. Some marine invertebrates react to ionizing radiation too, as by a snail's pulling in its tentacles or shellfish closing their shells. Mosquitoes, the small crustaceans called water fleas, fish, and turtles also change their behavior when ionizing radiation hits them.

Dr. Frank A. Brown of Northwestern University has reported interesting results in experiments with the planarian *Dugesia dorotocephala*, a common flatworm, exposed to gamma radiation.

Using a cesium 137 gamma-ray source, Brown and his colleagues studied radiation effects on the movement of the flatworms—and also on snails—during many months. It was established definitely that when the gamma radiation was increased to about six times that of the natural background radiation of gamma rays the worms turned away from the source. Apparently there is some sensing mechanism in the bodies of the worms that responds negatively to stimulation by gamma rays. Furthermore, it was found that the response varied depending on time of day and time of year. The "biological clock" seemed to affect the gamma radiation stimulus detected by the worm, or its response to the stimulus. This is an interesting parallel to studies in which it was learned that rats were more affected by X rays at night than during the day.

radiation and cell damage

Radiation can do biological damage. Antoine Becquerel was among the first to feel the power of radioactivity; a small capsule of radium given him by the Curies caused a painful burn to his flesh when he carried it in his vest pocket. Becquerel was lucky; he was quickly put on his guard against the danger. Other workers, including Marie Curie and her daughter, were not so fortunate. They died as a result of exposure over the years to the deadly radiation they worked with. A characteristic of X and gamma radiation is its accumulative nature—every slight bit that hits you leaves a lasting effect on your tissues, and if you add enough more throughout your life, you will accumulate enough effect for it to become actual damage.

Some pioneers did not understand about shielding themselves from X rays and gamma rays. Others were simply careless. In 1936 a plain stone monument was erected at the Roentgen Institute in Hamburg, Germany, dedicated "To the roentgenologists and radiologists of all the nations who

These cages, each containing about 200 honey bees, are about to be placed in a cell (tall cylinder in center) which will irradiate them with gamma rays from cobalt 60. Small groups of worker bees in laboratory tests using doses of 5,000 rads had their life spans reduced about 29 per cent by the radiation, yet entire colonies tested similarly in the field were wiped out. The production of honey, increasingly recognized as an important food, could be badly affected by nuclear fallout. *U. S. Atomic Energy Commission*

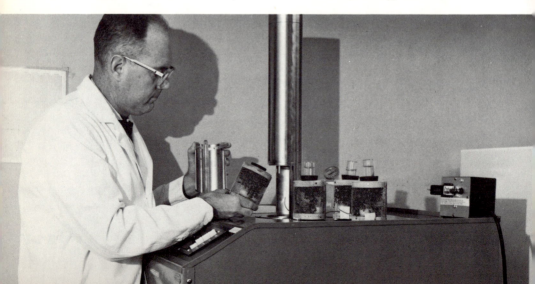

have given their lives in the struggle against the diseases of mankind." There were 110 names engraved on the stone at that time; others have been slowly added as the years go by. Use of radioactive materials in industry killed others than those in medicine and science. More than 40 women workers in watch factories died from wetting the tips of paint brushes with their tongues. These brushes were used to apply radium to watch hands and dials.

The coming of the atomic age led to the deaths of others from radioactivity. Some died in laboratories, like physicist Louis Slotin, who was exposed to killing radiation doing experiments on the bomb. There were many radiation victims at Hiroshima and Nagasaki, and some have died of accidental exposure in the years since then.

Most of the energy in radiation is given off as heat and for X rays a slight rise in temperature results. However, unless the living thing is very small, or the dose massive, not much damage is done by heat. It is the chemical change resulting from ionizing radiation that is deadly. Ionizing radiation has the ability to knock electrons from atoms in the cell; it creates ions or free radicals.

Matter is bound together within the atom by something called binding energy. The force between electrons amounts to a few electron volts. For this reason visible light, and its energy of less than three electron volts, causes no damage to cells. In the case of X rays and gamma rays, which are high-energy, ionizing radiation, the situation is drastically different. Chemical changes are made within molecules and this can have important consequences in industrial processes. Such chemical changes are even more important in living cells.

This tobacco plant received a gamma dose of 300 roentgens a day for six weeks. Its growth was stunted and tumors developed on the stem.

Four stages are involved when ionizing radiation penetrates living cells. The first is the "physical," in which energy is imparted to molecules of the matter penetrated by the radiation. The second stage is the "physicochemical," and secondary reactions take place. Ions collide and molecules are dissociated. Free radicals are formed during this stage. In the third, or "chemical" stage, these free radicals react with other material in the cell, actually producing new chemical compositions. These first three stages occur in a fraction of a second. There is a fourth stage, the body's response to the foreign chemicals produced by the ionizing radiation, and this stage may last for years.

Of great importance in studying the biological effects of radiation are the standards which have been set up. Two important measurement units come from names of pioneers in the field of radiation. The *curie* is that amount of radioactivity in which 37 billion atoms disintegrate per second. One pound of radium represents approximately 400 curies. The next unit is the *roentgen* (symbol, r), which is a measure of the actual X-ray or gamma-ray energy absorbed by air. One r produces two billion ion pairs in one cubic centimeter of air. (An ion pair is simply an ionized atom along with the electron that has been knocked off it. Once an atom has been ionized, changes start taking place in a cell.) For alpha and beta particles as well as gamma rays, a unit called the *rad* has come into use to define the dosage, or energy absorbed by tissue. One rad indicates 100 ergs of energy absorbed by a gram of irradiated substance. For practical purposes it is equivalent to a roentgen of X rays, since one roentgen indicates an absorbed dose of 0.93 to 0.98 rad.

It is generally thought that X-ray exposure should be held

to *no more than 50 roentgens in the first 30 years of life.* This is not difficult, since normal radiation exposure amounts to only about 6 roentgens in this period. Chest X rays in 30 years at one a year would amount to about 3 roentgens. Occupational exposure varies, and one writer sees an airlines pilot facing a number of radium-painted instrument dials as being exposed to an additional 10 roentgens in 30 years of flying. The following table indicates the amount of radiation, in rads, that an average person may pick up in a year from various sources.

NORMAL RADIATION

SOURCE	DOSE IN RADS
Natural	
External radiation	
Cosmic rays	0.028
Local gamma rays	0.047
Radon in air	0.001
Internal radiation	
Potassium 40	0.019
Carbon 14	0.001
Radon and disintegration products	0.002
Man-made	
Medical X rays	0.100
Watch and clock dials	0.001
Occupational exposure	0.002
TV sets	0.001
Fallout	0.001
Total exposure	0.203 rads per year

From the McGraw-Hill Encyclopedia
of Science and Technology

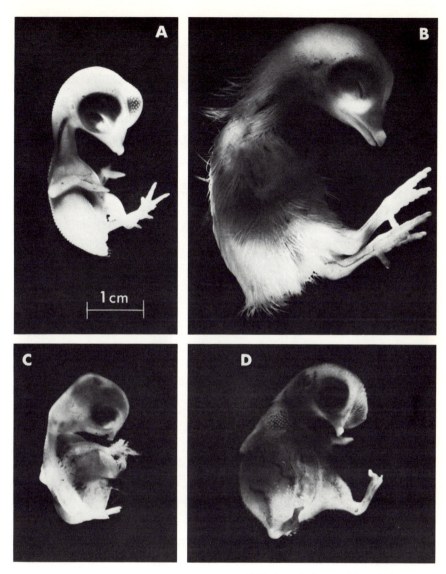

U. S. Atomic Energy Commission

Effects on chick development of irradiation with gamma rays. In picture A, a normal chick embryo ten days after fertilization. C shows a ten-day-old chick that was irradiated with gamma rays from cobalt 60 on the sixth day after fertilization; its shape is distorted by abnormal bone development, beak and toes are deformed, and there are swellings and hemorrhage spots in the skin. B shows a normal chick embryo 13 days after fertilization. D, also 13 days old, was irradiated on the sixth day; in addition to similar defects, its growth has been seriously stunted and development of feathers retarded.

Man can survive much more than the recommended exposure. This is particularly true of doses to individual parts of the body. However, exposure of the whole body to appreciable amounts of ionizing radiation can be fatal. The next table lists the approximate lethal, or killing, doses for various living things.

LETHAL DOSES OF X RADIATION

DOSE IN ROENTGENS

Man	400
Monkey	450
Rat	600
Mouse	400
Goldfish	750
Rabbit	800
Algae	4,000–8,500
Bacteria	5,000–130,000
Viruses	100,000–200,000
Protozoa	300,000

From *Atomic Radiation and Life* and the
McGraw-Hill Encyclopedia of Science and Technology

Unfortunately, some of us may have been exposed to more penetrating radiation than is good for us. For example, some doctors feel that thyroid cancer is increasing, and that it may be caused by the excessive pre-World War II X-ray treatments given for acne, tonsillitis, and other conditions in the chest, neck, or head.

Added to the danger of unnecessary medical X-ray exposure is that of faulty X-ray equipment. Surveys of some machines showed fluorescopes that were designed to emit 2 roentgens per minute producing more than 130 instead.

To enjoy the full blessings of medical X-ray diagnosis and therapy we must make every effort to safeguard ourselves against overexposure that may be more deadly than the disease we are trying to combat with X rays. Properly maintained equipment and adequate shielding for patients must be provided. Research is also being done on other ways to protect living cells against ionizing radiation.

One of the dangers can lie in certain television sets. The ordinary black-and-white set emits such slight amounts of X rays that they are of no real importance, but color TVs, which use much higher voltages, are in some cases improperly shielded and shoot radiation at a viewer in excessive amounts. In 1968 a government survey of color TVs in the area of Washington, D.C., found that 66 out of the 1,124 sets tested were something of a danger; the Public Health Service advised a viewing distance of six to ten feet, and avoiding prolonged exposure to the rear or sides of color TVs. The government can act legally to fine manufacturers of not only faulty color and projection TV sets, but also overstrong medical and dental X-ray machines (which produce about 90 per cent of all man-made radiation), microwave ovens, lasers, and other electronic products that produce radiation.

Since the introduction of atomic energy on a large scale, the demand for protection against radiation has increased. In addition to shielding, there are other possible methods. For example, it has been found that if the oxygen supply to cells is reduced there will be less radiation damage. This was known as early as 1910 when a piece of wood pressed against the skin protected somewhat against X-ray damage

Brookhaven National Laboratory

Both these originally identical groups of mice are 14 months old. The three above are the only surviving members of a group that was given a large radiation dose; they are gray-haired and senile, since radiation hastens aging. Control mice below are healthy and active.

while still permitting a photograph to be made. Lowering of temperature has also been demonstrated to lessen radiation damage. Unfortunately you can die of suffocation and freezing too, so the cure might seem as dangerous as the hazard itself. Chemical protection seems a more effective and practical approach. Certain amino acids, for example, protect the eyes from X-ray damage and sulfur-containing drugs taken internally afford protection for body cells against radiation damage. Much research is being conducted toward safeguarding man from radiation hazards, both on earth and during space flight.

genetic mutations

The few thousand volts of early X-ray equipment was sufficient to burn the tissue of patients and radiologists alike. Today high-powered laboratory and hospital equipment can kill malignant growths in patients. Long ago the American biologist Hermann Muller proved that X rays can also have much more subtle effects on the living cell. They can cause mutations, those drastic upsets of genetic material that are a principal cause of evolutionary changes.

Muller was born in 1890 and by the time he reached high school was so science-minded that he formed what was perhaps the first high school science club. Later, at Columbia University, Muller began work under Thomas Hunt Morgan, a recognized authority in the field of genetics.

Just after the turn of the century, genetics had become the object of much scientific investigation. Gregor Mendel had done interesting work with plants that pointed to a "blueprint" for future growth in the cell. The chromosomes, of

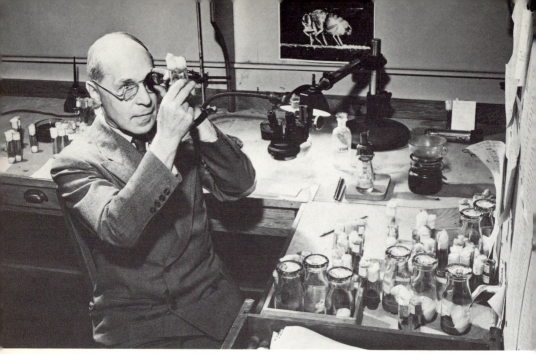

Dr. Hermann Muller, shown here in his laboratory, made biological history in the early 1920s by mutating fruit flies with X rays. On the bench before him are some of the milk bottles that served as cages for the flies.

which there are 46 in every human body cell, seemed a logical genetic mechanism, although these few factors could hardly account for all the various characteristics inherited from parents. Each chromosome was suspected of being made of even smaller units called genes.

To make his studies easier, Morgan studied the fruit fly, *Drosophila,* a simple life form possessing only eight chromosomes in each body cell. *Drosophila* is an insect that breeds with great rapidity, and Morgan was able to study many generations in a short period of time. Gradually he was able to show that mutations occurred in the animal world in similar fashion to that reported in the plant world. And indeed these changes seemed linked to the genes and chromosomes.

By 1919 Muller was speeding up the mutation studies by creating mutations, or at least hastening their occurrence. He used heat radiation. Somehow heat was able to influence the tiny genes within the *Drosophila* chromosomes. Later he decided that if heat worked, maybe other forms of radiation might have an effect too. Now Muller tried X rays. The result made genetic history and earned for Muller a Nobel Prize in medicine and physiology, although it was 1946 before his reward came, some 20 years after he had proved that X-ray radiation greatly increased the mutation rate in his fruit flies.

Muller reported that in 6,016 chromosomes with no X-ray irradiation only five lethal mutations occurred. Of 741 given four minutes of X-ray treatment, 59 lethal mutations occurred. And when 1,177 were irradiated for 48 minutes, the lethal mutations increased to 143. The percentages increased from about one-eighth of one per cent with no X rays to about 8 per cent with 24 minutes of X ray, and 12 per cent after 48 minutes.

In 1928 L. J. Stadler studied the effects of X rays on barley seedlings with similar mutation results. Many experiments were carried out in Sweden to induce beneficial mutations. In 1954 C. F. Konzak increased resistance to stem rust in oats, and in 1955 W. C. Gregory increased the yield of peanuts. However, it was necessary to irradiate 975,000 plants in Gregory's tests before a satisfactory new type of plant appeared.

Darwin's theory of evolution, in which the fittest species survives, required some mechanism to create occasional changes in species so that nature might slowly improve the breed. Mutation, or changing of the genetic blueprint, seemed

111

to be that mechanism. Genes have been found to be long, threadlike giant molecules, spirally wound. (Earlier microscope pictures of them at lower powers made it look as if they are separate units, like beads on a string, but this is an illusion. The electron microscope clearly shows the spiral winding.) Elimination of a single gene might have far-reaching effects on offspring. This was what Dr. Muller was seeking to prove when he irradiated fruit flies and then watched for changes in succeeding generations. He showed that his X irradiation of fruit flies caused an increase of mutations of about 15,000 per cent.

Mutations occur in nature partly as a result of radiation from outer space (the well-known cosmic rays), and apparently from radioactivity in the earth as well. Occasionally one of these high-energy rays strikes a gene and destroys it. Muller found that 99 per cent of mutations were harmful—fruit flies with no wings, for example, or men with incomplete arms or hands. The reason most mutations are a disadvantage is that each organism has developed through millions of years to a state of near-perfection for living in its

At left, a normal fruit fly. Irradiated fruit fly on right has underdeveloped wings. *Indiana University*

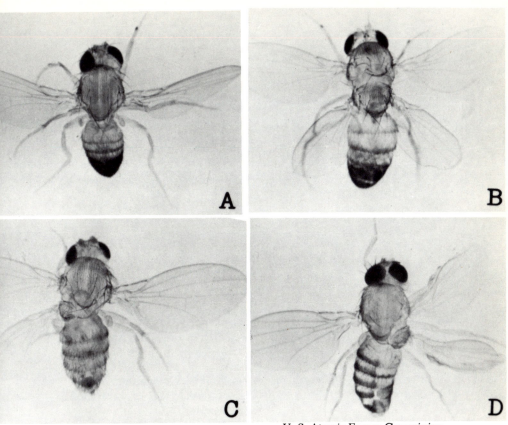

Radiation effects on fruit flies, as observed at the California Institute of Technology. A is a normal male; B has four wings instead of the usual two, as well as a double thorax, the body part behind the head. C and D have partially doubled thoraxes in distorted shapes, and three wings.

particular surroundings. Any sudden change made at random will almost surely disrupt things in some way, like a hammer dropped into a complicated machine. (For this reason Muller was a vigorous pioneer in warning doctors, dentists, and other X-ray users of the genetic dangers of carelessly used radiation.) However, one mutation out of a great many occasionally improves a species, and this is an important factor in the evolution of all plants and animals.

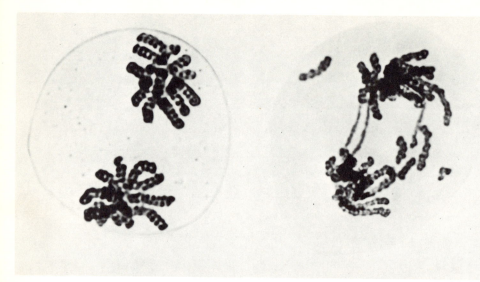

Brookhaven National Laboratory

At left, top, chromosomes of a normal plant cell in two groups; at right, the same kind of cell after exposure to X rays. The fragments and bridges between the groups are typical abnormalities produced by ionizing radiation. At bottom, chromosomes in a cell from a Chinese hamster after the cell was subjected to X rays. Chromosomes have doubled and tripled. *Argonne National Laboratory*

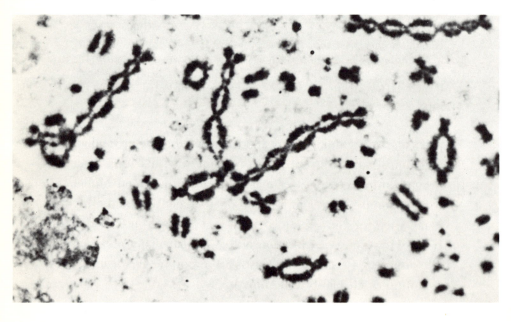

There are other means by which genes may be altered. Muller thought that an aging creature suffers natural damage to its genes. Chemicals also can affect the genes, as was tragically proved with the drug Thalidomide; more recently, LSD has been shown to damage the chromosomes of test animals and men, though biologists are still arguing about this. But radiation is believed to be the primary cause of mutations.

In 1967 Dr. Karl Z. Morgan, director of the Health Physics Division of Oak Ridge National Laboratory, told a congressional subcommittee that X-ray exposure of the unborn in animals can produce birth defects up to and including death. In humans, Dr. Morgan said, there was evidence that leukemia and other forms of cancer caused 40 per cent more deaths in children who had been exposed to X rays before being born, than in children not so exposed. Furthermore, Dr. Morgan said, for every observable damage there may be many other forms of unobservable damage, including genetic changes that may be passed on. Pointing out that about one-fifth of all mothers had been X-rayed while pregnant, Dr. Morgan urged the reduction of X-ray examination to a bare minimum. He felt this could be done with only one-tenth the strength of the doses now being given.

A survey of radiologists and their families indicates the danger in X rays. A total of 5,461 radiologists reported 14 per cent of abortions and stillbirths among their wives as compared with 12 per cent among 4,484 physicians not using radiation; and also 7 per cent of malformations compared with 5.5 per cent. Other statistics seem to show that radiologists live five years less than other doctors, as mentioned earlier.

The possibility has been raised that penetrating radiation might be used to cause human mutations of a beneficial nature, so that disease and weaknesses in the world would be eliminated. This was a particular dream of Dr. Muller. Such a hope seems very slim at this time. For the present, irradiation of plants, and insect and bacterial pests, looks much more hopeful.

8 pest control and food treatment

In 1916, research by the United States Department of Agriculture showed that if cigarette beetles were irradiated with X rays their eggs were not fertile. During the 1930s the idea occurred to Edward F. Knipling that it might be possible to eliminate the screwworm flies in the South by sterilizing them with radiation. Not until after World War II, when radioactive sources of cobalt 60 were available, was the idea put to work.

Using 2,500 roentgens of radiation from a cobalt source furnished by Oak Ridge National Laboratory, Knipling found that he could sterilize male flies. By the mid-1960s, billions of the insects had been bred, irradiated, and released. Within several years the entire population of flies in the South was virtually wiped out, at a cost of about one-third the annual damage done by the pests to crops.

By 1959 the battle of the screwworm flies was won in the

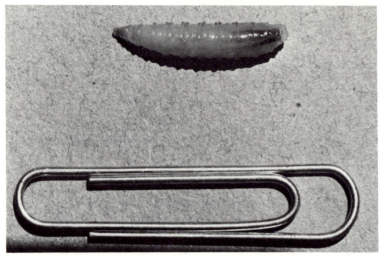

This is the small but devastating larva of the screwworm fly. Making these larvae sterile with radiation is an important weapon in combating them.

South. The idea had also been demonstrated on Curaçao in the Netherlands Antilles. In the 1960s an eradication program was carried out in Texas and Mexico. On Rota island, in the Marianas in the Pacific, not screwworm flies but melon flies were wiped out by radiation sterilization. Plans for similar pest eradication include fruit flies in Hawaii and the larvas that cause trichinosis.

X rays or gamma rays can be used for these purposes, but gamma rays are more attractive. Large supplies of gamma radiation are becoming available in the waste materials from nuclear reactors. It would seem far better to make use of this material than to spend huge sums of money burying it in deep pits or far at sea. Bags or other containers of radioactive waste, properly placed, would give long-time protection in warehouses and other storage areas by constantly penetrating stored food and other materials with radiation, killing any pests they may contain.

Civil Defense authorities and many others are greatly concerned about the possible contamination of food and water supplies in the event of atomic war. In fact, courses are taught in decontamination of such supplies. Happily, it is being learned that lesser amounts of the radiation from nuclear sources can be used not to contaminate food but to preserve it. Since earliest times, one of man's great problems has been providing himself with a steady supply of food rather than relying on killing game or picking food as needed. While there was some success with such simple methods as sun-drying certain foods, it was not until Pasteur explained the

Here a livestock owner collects screwworm maggots for laboratory identification from the open wound they have caused in the hide of an animal.   *U. S. Department of Agriculture*

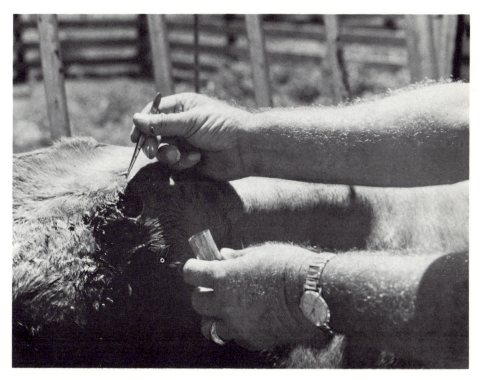

cause of spoiling in foods and developed the heat sterilization we call pasteurization that real progress was made.

Food is generally infested with a multitude of tiny life
forms. While some of these are not harmful to man, in time
they cause spoiling. Heat in the proper amount can kill these
pests, and so can cold. We use both ends of the temperature
scale to protect our food from attack. Doses of radiation
will also kill bacteria, and it is to this approach that science
is now turning. Even those products which are sterilized
with heat must then be kept cold or at least cool because all
the germs are not really killed. Refrigeration is expensive and
bothersome, as we find out on a picnic, or when the power
fails and the family has a freezer full of stored meat. Beaming
a ray of ionizing radiation at the food can kill the trouble-
makers for good. Then the food will keep for long periods of
time at ordinary temperature.

Studies of irradiating food as a substitute for pasteurization
or freezing began in 1943. The Massachusetts Institute of
Technology pioneered food-radiation research during World
War II, but progress was slow. In 1951 the U. S. Army
Quartermaster Corps began its research program along the
same lines but used the newly available radioactive materials
produced in atomic energy research. Army work produced
results that were not as successful as hoped for, and after
eight years the food-irradiation program was halted.

The United Nations became interested in the question,
and in 1958 held a meeting in England. Seventeen European
governments sent representatives. Although the process has
not yet come of age, interest has revived. In the United States
a number of universities, industrial firms, and government
agencies support active programs.

plants and gamma

At Brookhaven National Laboratories on Long Island, New York, experiments have been conducted for several years by exposing plants in a large field to gamma radiation. This is provided by a slug of cobalt 60 which emits 2,000 curies. This is the equivalent of radiation from about five pounds of radium, almost as much of that material as has been produced to date.

The cobalt 60 source is mounted on a pole for most of the day and beams strong gamma radiation all about it. Then it is lowered fifteen feet into the ground so that scientists can tend the plants. (One time the mechanism for lowering the source failed and a rifleman had to enter the dangerous field and shoot the chain that held it up. He had to work quickly because of the intense radiation, but succeeded in hitting the chain with his second shot.)

So strong is the radiation that pine trees a thousand feet from the source were killed. However, in scientifically controlled mutation experiments gamma radiation has produced peach trees that ripen earlier than normal varieties; low-growing cereal grasses that weather windstorms better; a blight resistant corn; as well as high-yield peanuts and beans.

Scientists put to good use the lessons learned in tests like those at Brookhaven. Because of its biological effects, radiation can be used to kill tissue in sprouting vegetables. This technique has extended the storage life of such vegetables as potatoes, beans, carrots, artichokes, beets, turnips, and onions. Using cobalt 60 gamma rays, researchers found that 4,000

Snapdragon plants are arranged at different distances from a source of cesium 137, which shoots gamma rays at them 20 hours a day. While a human being is inside this shielded room, the cesium 137 is lowered inside the pipe into a shielded container below the floor.

rads were sufficient to stop sprouting in onions, and 20,000 rads in potatoes.

Fruits and vegetables can also be treated by irradiation to prevent spoilage by pests, molds, and yeast. Beans, corn, cabbage, peas, asparagus, broccoli, tomatoes, and spinach are among the vegetables that have been successfully irradiated for storage. Irradiation of 200,000 rads is used. Apples, berries, grapes, peaches, citrus fruits, and pears have also been treated.

Milk has been irradiated too, and demonstrated to be as safe and flavorful as that kept fresh by other methods. Bakery products have been irradiated. Bread reacts beneficially to the treatment and its storage life is extended. However, pastries react poorly because of their high fat content. And it was found that there was danger of the creation of off-odors and flavors from the plastic wrappings used around bakery products.

Spent rods from nuclear reactors are used to furnish gamma rays for food irradiation. Complete sterilization is accomplished with from one million to seven million rads. Radiation will penetrate glass jars and metal cans so that sterilization can be done after packaging.

"Radiopasteurization" instead of full sterilization can be done at much lower radiation levels. In one example, hamburger was irradiated with 500,000 to 1,000,000 rads. This reduced the bacterial count from one million per gram of weight to only one thousand per gram. The meat could then be kept in storage for one year instead of only one week.

There are a number of diseases affecting humans that are carried in our food. An example is trichinosis, caused by the parasitic worm *Trichinella*, which develops from larvae deposited in pork. It was found that a dose of 1,000,000 rads killed all *Trichinella* but ruined the flavor of the meat. So lower doses—up to 15,000—were given to stop larval development and to sterilize females. This has no detrimental effect on flavor or odor.

At about 15,000 rads irradiation begins to change the odor of food. At 100,000 rads detrimental flavor changes occur and when a dose of 1,000,000 rads is approached, texture and color also are changed.

Research indicates that the best time for irradiating pork to control *Trichinella* is during the cooling period at the slaughterhouse. Using cobalt 60, cesium 137, or fuel slugs from a nuclear reactor, a dose of 30,000 rads could be given for a cost of less than a cent per pound of treated meat.

Poultry and fish as well as red meats have been successfully irradiated for preservation. The problem is in the change in flavor caused in some meats. For instance, sea foods are generally unacceptable in flavor after sufficient radiation to kill the organisms that spoil them. Steak too is unacceptable after high radiation doses. However, ham, salami, sausage, and bologna do not appear to suffer from flavor changes. Chicken actually improves in flavor when it is not necessary to store it at freezing temperatures.

the safety question

Are irradiated foods, even if they are flavorful and fresh, good for humans to eat? Most but not all scientists think so. They have carefully checked three important questions. First, do irradiated foods lose their nutritive value; second, are they poisonous; third, is there any danger of mutations in those who eat them? Tests with animals fed such foods indicate a

124

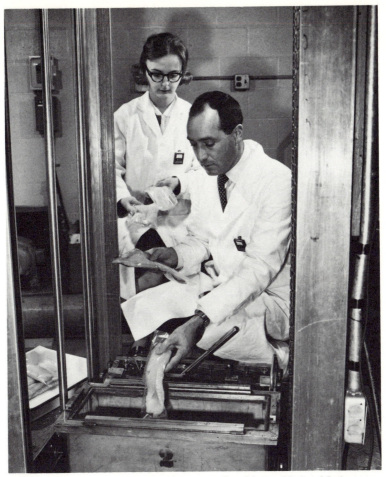

Placing fresh fish filets in a cobalt 60 irradiator at the Massachusetts Institute of Technology in experiments to preserve food by radiation. The irradiator was designed at the Brookhaven National Laboratory in Long Island, New York.

slight vitamin deficiency, but this can be made up with supplements. And several generations of animals have been tested with diets of irradiated food with no toxic effects. Humans have lived entirely on such foods for appreciable periods of time with no bad effects detected in subsequent annual examinations.

On June 26, 1956, the members of the Joint Congressional Committee on Atomic Energy attended a banquet at which the food was unusual: every bit of it was irradiated. None of the many diners suffered any known harmful aftereffects, nor have thousands of other people who have voluntarily eaten irradiated foods.

In the matter of possible mutations, the picture appears to be fairly good also, but caution seems necessary. Dr. Francis McKinney of the Oak Ridge National Laboratory says that rats and dogs fed for over two years with irradiated foods showed no defects from the food, nor did their offspring. Dr. B. S. Schweigert of Michigan State University, who has reviewed many tests of this kind, says that results to date confirm this optimism, but adds that he knows of no scientist involved in such experiments who goes so far as to say that "food irradiation is 100 per cent safe." Inevitably there seem to be few or no "hundred per cents" in biological testing, for some individual organisms are always different enough to have an unexpected reaction. Dr. Garret Hardin of the University of California feels that "on the basis of the present inconclusive evidence" it is a hazard to encourage a food-irradiation industry.

And to back up his doubt, there are university and government researches showing that rats fed with irradiated food had a lower birthrate, an increase in stillbirths, developed cataracts in their eyes, and cancerous tumors in their bodies. Dogs were shown to lose weight, and the females had fewer pups. There was also some reason to believe that gamma-treated food made nonirradiated food less nourishing when the two types were mixed.

Clearly, the total picture is uncertain. Considering the many decades it took to catch up with all the injury from careless use of X-ray machines (a still unfinished story), making haste slowly seems a wise thing to do.

What are the prospects of irradiating water as well? In some cases water is now sterilized with ultraviolet rays. As gamma radiation becomes more available as a waste by-product of power production perhaps we will sterilize with it. Even sewage may be so treated to guard against disease. Dr. James E. Etzel of Purdue University has developed a sewage treatment with gamma rays that he says would save cities much money, as well as reduce air pollution and odor.

Medicine and surgical supplies can also be sterilized by radiation. Antibiotics can be so treated with no loss in potency, although vitamins are changed. The radiation of blood and tissues being stored for transfusion and transplants has also been suggested.

9   radiation experiments

Improperly used, X and gamma rays are dangerous. But it is possible to conduct safe laboratory experiments in science classes that demonstrate some of the things we have been discussing in this book. A strong word of warning: PERFORM THESE EXPERIMENTS WITH THE HELP OF YOUR SCIENCE TEACHER! (If you are *really* an advanced amateur experimenter with lots of experience, you can do them safely yourself if you know the rules of self-protection, and remain constantly alert.)

In this chapter we describe a number of experiments within the ability of science-minded readers. These range from simple light diffraction with a prism to the construction and operation of a low-power X-ray generator. Radiography experiments are covered as well as irradiation of living specimens.

the spectrum

A simple but rewarding radiation experiment can be made with nothing more than a glass prism which will break white light from the sun or some other source into literally all the colors of the rainbow. This is a repetition of Newton's famous experiment. Prisms can be purchased from suppliers shown in the appendix.

Block off all the light at the windows except for a narrow slit cut in a piece of black paper. Place the prism so that this light beam passes through it. On the far wall place a piece of white paper on which the spectrum will be shown. Red rays will make a band at one end of the spectrum on your paper; violet rays will be the last visible band at the other. These electromagnetic waves, remember, are only a very small part of the entire spectrum of such waves. If you could see them, infrared rays would show up beyond the red, and ultraviolet beyond the violet. With a thermometer you might be able to detect the former; if you repeat the experiments of Ritter, the ultraviolet rays will leave their mark.* Assuming that other waves could be projected by a prism, radio waves would be higher yet on the sheet of paper above the visible spectrum, and X rays and gamma rays, far to the bottom—*if* you had a strip of paper long enough to take in the entire spectrum.

electroscope

A glass jar will serve nicely as the housing for a rough electroscope, since we need something transparent to see the leaves of the instrument react to electric charges. A circular piece of thin, dry wood, or even cardboard, is fitted over the top of the jar. Force a piece of heavy copper wire through the

---

* An ordinary prism will pass relatively little ultraviolet; quartz glass passes much more. Photographic paper—enlarging or contact—may be simpler to work with than film, which is easily fogged by a slight bit of stray light.

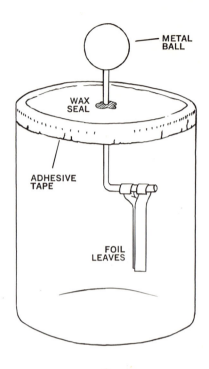

A homemade electroscope

center of the wood or cardboard so that about two inches of
it protrudes into the bottle and about one inch remains above
the top of the wood. Bend the bottom end of the wire at
right angles.

For the leaves of the electroscope use light aluminum foil
strips about an inch long and one-eighth inch wide. Bend a
U in the end of each piece of foil so that it will hang over the
bent end of the wire. They may hang next to each other
along the wire, but there will be a little more sensitivity if
you twist them slightly so the flat parts of the strips are face
to face.

Keep the inside of the jar dry by sealing the edge tightly with adhesive tape and melting a little wax around the wire at its entry-hole. Now attach a tightly crumpled ball of aluminum foil about half an inch in diameter to the top of the wire, and the electroscope is complete. (Variants for the knob might be a large steel ball bearing, a steel marble, or even a smooth doorknob. Whatever the ball is, it must have metallic contact with the wire. With some ingenuity you could suspend two short hairs or antennas of a dead insect in place of foil strips, for greater sensitivity.)

Run a comb through your hair and touch the ball of the electroscope. Electrons from the comb will run down the wire and into the leaves of foil, giving them each a negative charge of electricity so that they repel each other and fly apart. (They will do the same if the rod merely approaches the knob also, though in this case the charge affects the knob across space.) Slowly the charge will leak away and the leaves will drop to the neutral charge position. By rubbing a glass rod with silk and holding the rod near the ball of the instrument you can charge the leaves positively, since electrons will travel from the leaves to the glass rod.

The physicist Victor Hess showed that there must be a source of radiation from space that caused his electroscope to lose its charge. Our homemade instrument is not this sensitive, but we can detect stronger radiation in the form of a radium dial watch face. Charge the leaves negatively with your comb and then place the watch, face down, over the ball of the electroscope without quite touching it. You will find that the leaves lose their charge more rapidly with the radium near the electroscope, indicating that it is a source of charged particles.

Geiger counter

A better detector of gamma rays is a Geiger counter. Inexpensive models may be purchased but you can build a portable one, powered by a small six-volt battery, and use it to detect not only gamma radiation but also beta rays and cosmic rays. This is described in detail in the book *Atomic Energy*, by Irene Jaworski and Alexander Joseph. Here's what you'll need:

1	700- or 800-volt Geiger counter tube
1	output transformer from a radio speaker
1	push button switch (doorbell type will do)
1	6-volt battery
1	set of earphones
1	0.25 microfarad, 600-volt capacitor
1	0.002 microfarad bypass capacitor
1	2-megohm resistor
6	binding posts (The two for the spark gap should preferably be the set-screw type with horizontal holes for the nails.)
2	small nails (for spark gap)
1	board about 6 inches square
	Wire for hooking up the circuit

You should be able to get all of these from your local radio supply dealer, except for the Geiger tube. See the appendix for a supplier of this item.

Assemble the circuit as shown in the drawing. (In this case the transformer is used in an unusual way, with the secondary on the battery side.) The points of the nails in

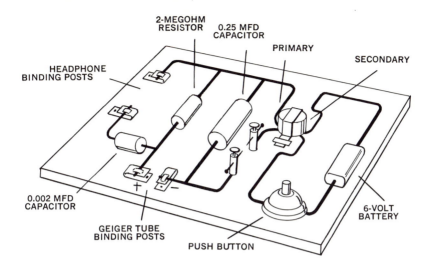

The diagram labels:

2-MEGOHM RESISTOR

0.25 MFD CAPACITOR

PRIMARY

SECONDARY

HEADPHONE BINDING POSTS

0.002 MFD CAPACITOR

6-VOLT BATTERY

GEIGER TUBE BINDING POSTS

PUSH BUTTON

With this simple circuit and a Geiger tube you can make your own Geiger counter. Redrawn from Jaworski and Joseph, *Atomic Energy*.

the spark-gap mechanism should be about 1/16 inch apart. When all connections are made, put the whole assembly in a plastic box to avoid accidental shocks. A hole should be made in the plastic above the Geiger tube so radiations will hit it directly. Now the counter is ready to operate. Charge it by pushing the button 15 to 20 times. Put on the earphones and you should hear a "background" clicking in them.

The background count comes from all sources of radiation: cosmic and earth radioactivity. If you wrap a sheet of lead ⅛ inch thick about the Geiger tube this will shield it from all radiation but cosmic rays and you can then count the cosmic-radiation clicks.

To test artificial sources, such as radium dials, cathode ray tubes, and so on, simply listen and make a count. Then subtract the known background count and you will know the amount of artificial radiation, consisting of beta and gamma rays. Alpha rays will not penetrate the Geiger tube so you will not be able to detect these. To count gamma rays only, wrap the Geiger tube in sheet aluminum or heavy aluminum foil. This stops the beta rays, which are not as penetrating, and you will then be able to measure the gamma count over the background. Detailed instructions on making another Geiger counter may be found in *Scientific American* for May 1960, p. 112.

scintillation viewer

We cannot see X rays or gamma rays directly, of course, but we can detect them with our eyes by watching the "scintillation" or tiny sparking effect of certain substances when they are struck by radiation. Zinc sulphide is a scintillator, and it flashes when struck by radiation such as that from radium. You can buy a device called a spinthariscope at a very low price, or you can make one yourself.

The spinthariscope consists of a cardboard tube about six inches long and one and a half to two inches wide. Inside this insert a smaller cardboard tube fitted with a magnifying lens. The insides of both tubes should be painted dull black. This tube should slide snugly and smoothly within the larger one, as in the picture. (The large tube may have to be shortened

A spinthariscope, or scintillation viewer, shows the "sparks" induced in zinc sulphide by radiation from a bit of radium or a similar substance.

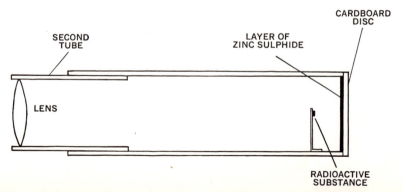

somewhat, depending on the lens you use.) On the end of the bigger tube is a fluorescent screen. This is a disc of cardboard cut to fit the end, covered on the inside with transparent tape sticky on both sides (or, as a substitute, a thin coat of shellac). Zinc sulphide is dusted on the tape or fresh shellac (avoid inhaling the powder). A source of radiation, such as a piece of the number cut from a radium watch dial, is glued to the top of a narrow bit of cardboard fastened within the large tube about half an inch or less from the screen end. (Handle the dial and number with tweezers only, not fingers.) Now the screen is fastened, sulphide inward, over the end of the tube, with a tight seal against light.

When it is complete, hold the spinthariscope to your eye and look through the lens, which may be adjusted for best focus. As your eye becomes used to the dark, it should see the scintillations, or flashes, on the screen as it is bombarded by the radioactive material. You are now seeing, at second hand, radiation that is invisible under normal conditions.

The construction of the spinthariscope is presented in *Scientific American* for March 1953, p. 104.

cloud chamber

It was C. T. R. Wilson's pioneer cloud chamber that first made the tracks of radiation visible. You can make a simple cloud chamber yourself and see such tracks, although a homemade instrument is not sensitive enough to detect the tiny squiggles of gamma rays. Inexpensive chamber kits are available.

Our cloud chamber will be a peanut butter jar, one with straight sides and a wide mouth. Cut a one-inch-wide piece

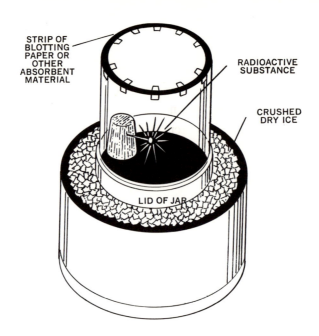

STRIP OF BLOTTING PAPER OR OTHER ABSORBENT MATERIAL

RADIOACTIVE SUBSTANCE

CRUSHED DRY ICE

LID OF JAR

A homemade cloud chamber as set up for observing alpha rays, with a radioactive source mounted inside.

of weather stripping, heavy felt, or blotting paper, and fasten it with small bits of adhesive tape around the bottom of the jar, inside, as shown. Inside the lid of the jar fit a circle of black velvet or velveteen, holding it with a little cement (which must dry *thoroughly*).

Pour some rubbing alcohol into the jar—enough to saturate the absorbent strip and moisten the bottom of the jar. Now put the lid on tightly. Next a cold base is needed. Make a false bottom of cardboard to fit inside a pound coffee can or something similar. On top of the cardboard put an inch or so of crushed dry ice, or a smooth cake of it. (Ordinary ice will *not* do the job.) Place the cloud chamber, upside down, on the dry ice, so you can observe through the glass bottom and sides.

The glass top of the chamber remains near room temperature and you can assist it by placing your hand on it to warm it slightly. Meanwhile, the metal lid gets cold from contact with the dry ice so that there is a temperature difference of perhaps 150 degrees F. from top to bottom. Now the alcohol vapor begins to make a fine fog that will track particles passing through it. Shine the light from a focusing flashlight or a home slide projector through the chamber from one side and begin a patient watch.

If cosmic rays are penetrating the chamber, their vapor trails should show up as starlike clusters or faint, disconnected, beadlike strings. However, most of the tracks will be from earth radiation. To detect artificial radiation, place a source of rays near the chamber. Again, a radium watch face will do. If it is outside the chamber, only beta trails will show inside. To see the alpha tracks you must put the radioactive material inside the chamber.

Cloud chamber projects are described in the following issues of *Scientific American*: September 1952, p. 179; April 1956, p. 156; December 1956, p. 169; and June 1959, p. 113; also in C. L. Stong's *Scientific American Book of Projects for the Amateur Scientist*.

x-ray and gamma photographs

The simplest way of detecting radiation is with a piece of camera film. Just as visible light causes the silver compound to darken, X rays and gamma rays will also. Place a piece of film, protected in black paper, on the screen of your TV set and leave it there while the set is on. After a total operating time of about 10 hours, remove the film and either develop it yourself if you can or have it developed. If there are dark tracks on the film, X rays are present. You can use this same technique to make X-ray pictures of a variety of objects.

Thorium is a radioactive material and you can get some by buying a mantle for a gasoline lantern such as a Coleman lantern. Remove the clothlike material and flatten it out. Place it on a piece of film protected in black paper or, more simply, just unroll a roll of film in the dark until you feel the negative material. Place the mantle against the film and re-wind the paper about it. Tape it securely and leave it for about a week. When the film is developed you should see a radioautograph of the mantle.

Other commonly available materials are slightly radioactive too. For example, some Fiesta Ware dishes are glazed with uranium oxide. A bright orange dish or saucer of this ware can be used to make pictures of metal objects on film. Place a piece of film in a protective black envelope. Over it put a paper clip or some other metal object. Over this place the Fiesta Ware dish. Leave this for two weeks and then have the film developed. The beta and gamma rays should have exposed the film except where the metal object blocked them. (These dishes are safe for food, the radiation being very weak.)

You can use the same technique with a radium dial watch. If you place just the watch on the film it should leave a picture of the hands and numbers if they are really radio-active. (Some dials use phosphor paints; these will have no effect.) Or you can place the watch above some object to be photographed (put it in an envelope above the black wrapped film). After a week or so have the film developed.

Radioactive ore samples can also be checked with film. In

fact, uranium prospectors have used this method of locating the valuable material. They simply left rolls of film in suspected areas for a week or so and then had them developed. Any that showed streaks indicated a probable uranium find.

producing cathode rays

There is an easy way to produce cathode rays, and possibly X rays too, with inexpensive materials. Get a burned-out clear glass bulb (100 to 200 watts). This will be your cathode-ray tube. To supply it with high-voltage electricity you will need a six-volt battery and an ignition coil from an old automobile (one from a Model-T Ford is best). A simple on-off switch and some hook-up wire complete the list of materials.

Wrap one end of a bared wire about the base of the bulb. The other end attaches to the vibrator end of the ignition coil. Tape a small square of aluminum foil to the other end of the bulb and attach another wire to the foil. The opposite end of this wire goes to the A terminal on the coil. Now connect the battery to the switch and coil as shown.

Close the switch. (To avoid a shock—uncomfortable though not dangerous—don't touch the bulb or coil.) High voltage will cause a stream of electrons to travel from the base of the bulb to the aluminum foil. These may be violet colored instead of the weird green that Roentgen saw when he did his famous experiment, but they are cathode rays nevertheless. You can prove this by using a strong magnet to bend the cathode ray stream.

Weak X rays may be produced and you might detect these with film or other methods described. Because of possible X radiation, keep your distance as much as possible and don't experiment too long.

x-ray generator

To conduct actual biological and other experiments with X rays, you may want to build your own generator. Commercial or industrial equipment is expensive but you can purchase a television high-voltage rectifier tube, which incidentally produces X rays, and use it in a setup worked out by Dr. Alexander Joseph. You have read that some television sets can be hazardous to viewers because they beam X rays out of the cabinet. Proper shielding guards against this condition, of course.

An automobile ignition coil can be used in producing cathode rays in an old light bulb. Redrawn from Jaworski and Joseph, *Atomic Energy*.

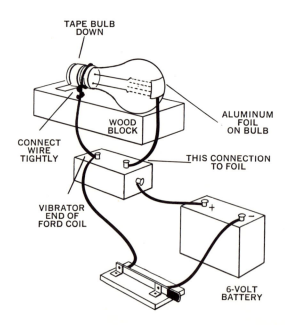

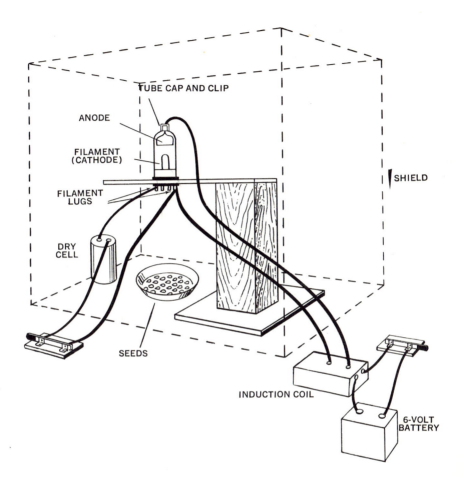

This simple setup, designed by Alexander Joseph, gives you your own X-ray generator. Redrawn from *Senior Scholastic*.

Purchase a tube—it can be a 1G-3 or 1B-3 (2 Z-2/G84). Before doing anything with it, *remind yourself that it produces X rays and is potentially hazardous.* Before you operate it, it must be completely enclosed in a steel shield or a wooden box lined with sheet lead that is at least 1/16 inch thick.

Mount a tube socket appropriate for this tube on a thin piece of lucite or other clear plastic so that the cap on top of the tube faces upward; the anode will then send X rays downward, which is safest. The socket should be about 10 inches above the base or table top.

A six-volt battery wired to the primary connections of an ignition coil (see preceding project) and fitted with a switch provides the high voltage for the cathode and anode of the tube (see drawing). Ignition wire meant for connecting car spark plugs should be used between the coil and the tube. (Naturally, be sure the coil is not operating when connecting the tube.) Connect the secondary terminal of the ignition coil that is farthest away from the coil's vibrator with one of the filament lugs on the tube socket. (A clerk at the radio store where you buy the tube can tell you which socket lugs are which.) Connect the other secondary terminal with the anode cap on top of the tube by means of a clip that you can buy for a few cents in the store.

Now connect wires from the two filament lugs to a dry cell or a filament transformer giving in either case 1.25 volts —no more or less. (You may have to use a small resistor to get this exact value from an ordinary cell; or use a mercury cell.) *Once the shield is over the assembly,* the switch may be thrown on and the tube will begin to beam X rays down through and around the socket onto any object placed on the table below it. You can check for X rays with a piece of photographic film. Wrap the film in protective black paper so that light will not expose it. Time all your experimental exposures with a watch or kitchen timer.

Among the living things you can irradiate are bread molds, seeds, paramecia and other protozoans, frog eggs, and so on, testing the radiation effect on their rate of growth, and also seeing if you can induce some mutations.

For the advanced experimenter, a more powerful X-ray generator is described in *Scientific American* for July 1965, page 135 (or see Stong's *Amateur Scientist* book mentioned in the cloud-chamber project).

x-ray botany

A fertile field for X-ray experiments is the irradiation of the seeds of various plants. Radiation botany is a fascinating study and dates back to at least 1908. Millions of mutations have been induced artificially in laboratories. While most of these were not beneficial or of the type to be perpetuated, there have been several that led to better strains of plants, including beans and peanuts.

You can use the X-ray equipment already described, or as suggested by the U. S. Atomic Energy Commission, try ultraviolet irradiation of plants. An eight-watt germicidal ultraviolet light costs about two dollars, yet produces mutations in plants comparable to those of X rays and gamma rays.

Another method is to purchase irradiated seeds from a supplier of scientific materials and compare their growth with that of "control" seeds which have not been irradiated. Free booklets from the Atomic Energy Commission that are helpful are "What Can You Expect from Atomic-Irradiated Seeds?" and "Experiments with Radiation on Seeds," Numbers 1 and 2. Turtox Service Leaflet No. 53, "Experiments in Radiobiology," is also useful. To obtain these, see the section "Further Reading."

radioisotopes

Radiation experiments may also be conducted with isotopes such as phosphorus 32 and iodine 131, mentioned earlier. Kits are available for these isotopes, and they are of sufficient strength to be detected by Geiger counters or other detectors. The booklet *Laboratory Experiments with Radioisotopes for High School Science Demonstrations* is published by the Atomic Energy Commission. This is listed in "Further Reading."

glossary

alpha particle: A helium nucleus that is one of the three products of spontaneous disintegration of radioactive material. Has a positive charge.

angiograph: X-ray picture made by injecting an opaque dye into blood vessels.

angstrom unit: Measurement unit of wavelengths; most commonly used for light. One hundred-millionth of a centimeter.

anode: The positive electrode or terminal of an electrical circuit.

autoradiograph: A self-photograph of radioactive material. Sometimes called radioautograph.

background radiation: Natural radiation from cosmic rays and terrestrial sources.

beta particle: An electron that is one of three products of spontaneous disintegration of radioactive material. Has a negative charge.

bubble chamber: A container holding superheated liquid in which particle tracks are shown by the formation of tiny bubbles.

cathode: The negative electrode or terminal of an electrical circuit.

145

cloud chamber: Instrument for detection of radiation through its tracks in vapor within the chamber.

cobalt "bomb": Radioactive gamma-ray source used to treat disease.

Crookes tube: A vacuum tube fitted with electrodes for study of effects of current on molecules of gas.

curie: A unit of the radiation from one gram of radium; equal to 37 billion atom disintegrations per second.

electromagnetic radiation: Energy transmitted through space or material in the form of electrical and magnetic waves vibrating at right angles to each other.

electron: An elementary particle which carries a negative electrical charge. The lightest known charged particle.

electron volt: A unit of energy; the change in electrical potential amounting to one volt in an electron.

fluorescence: The absorption of radiation and re-emission at a longer wavelength.

fluoroscope: A screen that fluoresces in X radiation.

free radical: An atom or molecule having one or more unpaired electrons. Normally part of a combination and created only by special conditions such as ionizing radiation.

frequency: The number of waves or vibrations per second.

gamma ray: Electromagnetic radiation from radioactive substance.

Geiger counter: Electrical device for measuring radiation.

Geissler tube: A vacuum tube, similar to the Crookes tube, for studying electrical discharges.

hard X rays: Very short-wave, highly penetrating radiation.

Hertzian waves: Radio waves.

Hittorf tube: Electrically charged vacuum tube, similar to Crookes and Geissler tubes.

infrared light: Invisible radiation, lower in frequency than visible red light.

ion: An atom, molecule, or free radical that has acquired an electric charge because of the loss or gain of an electron or electrons.

ionizing radiation: Radiation, including X rays and gamma rays, with the ability to charge atoms electrically.

irradiation: The process of bombarding a specimen or organism with radiation.

light: Electromagnetic radiation, generally that which is visible to the eye.

micron: Unit of length used in measuring waves. One-thousandth of a millimeter.

Mössbauer effect: Absorption of gamma radiation without recoil by a nucleus so that the waves are re-emitted at the same wavelength.

mutation: A genetic change in a living thing; induced naturally or with man-made radiation.

neutron: An uncharged (neutral) part of an atomic nucleus.

nucleus: Central, positively charged portion of an atom. Except in hydrogen, it consists of protons and neutrons.

opaque: Absorbent of a particular radiation.

optics: The study of light and its properties.

particle accelerator: Electromagnetic device that accelerates sub-atomic particles. Used to produce radiation.

particle theory: Belief that radiation consists of particles or "corpuscles" of energy.

penetrating radiation: High-energy radiation capable of piercing matter to some depth.

photon: A quantum of light. Smallest unit of light energy.

Planck's constant: Ratio of a quantum of radiant energy to its frequency.

prism: Triangular-shaped piece of glass or other transparent material that refracts light.

process radiation: The use of X rays and gamma rays in industrial chemistry, food processing, etc.

proton: A positive part of an atomic nucleus.

quantum: Tiny "packet" or "bundle" of energy; the elemental unit of energy in radiation.

rad: Unit of alpha and beta radiation dosage absorbed by tissue; equal to 100 ergs per gram of tissue.

radiation: Energy emitted in the form of electromagnetic waves or charged particles.

radioactivity: The disintegration of atoms, either spontaneously or artificially, which releases radiation, including gamma rays.

radiograph: A photograph made by radiation, especially X rays or gamma rays.

radioisotope: Radioactive or unstable form of an element.

radiologist: Doctor trained in the application of X rays and other penetrating radiation for diagnosis and therapy.

radio waves: Electromagnetic waves with frequencies from about 10 thousand to 100 million cycles per second.

radium: Radioactive element isolated by the Curies.

rep: Roentgen Equivalent Physical. Varies from 90 to 110 ergs per gram, depending on tissue irradiated.

roentgen: Measurement of X-ray and gamma-ray radiation. One roentgen produces two billion pairs of ions in one cubic centimeter of dry air. Symbol, r.

roentgenologist: A specialist in the use of X rays for diagnosis and therapy.

scintillation counter: A device that detects and registers radiation.

secondary X rays: X rays produced by reflection in bombarding material or tissue by primary X rays.

shielding: Metal or other protection from radiation.

soft rays: Longer-wave, less penetrating radiation.

spectrograph: Instrument for photographing the spectrum.

spectroscope: Instrument for viewing the spectrum.

spectrum: Series of radiant energies arranged in order of wavelength or frequency.

spinthariscope: Instrument for viewing the scintillations or light flashes from radiation striking a fluorescing screen.

target: Metal, such as tungsten, from which electron-stream bombardment produces X rays; also, anything at which radiation is directed.

ultraviolet: Invisible light waves with a shorter wavelength than the visible violet.

wave theory: Belief that electromagnetic radiation consists of waves of energy rather than individual particles.

X rays: Penetrating radiation produced by electrons bombarding a target, generally of metal.

X-ray diffraction: The "bending" of X rays on passage through a crystal.

X-ray star: A star which emits radiation predominantly in the X-ray spectrum.

scientific-equipment suppliers

American Basic Science Club, Inc., 104 Heimann St., San Antonio, Texas 78205
Cloud chambers, electroscopes, radioactive materials, spectroscopes, spinthariscopes, ultraviolet lamps

Edmund Scientific Company, 300 Edscorp Bldg., Barrington, New Jersey 08007
Prisms, infrared sources, ultraviolet sources, diffraction gratings, transformers, batteries, Van de Graaff generators, Tesla coils, atomic energy labs, cloud chambers, spinthariscopes, autoradiograph materials, irradiated seed kits, spectroscopes

Electronic Products, Inc., 11 East Third St., Mount Vernon, New York
Geiger tubes

Firms selling isotope kits

Abbott Laboratories, Oak Ridge Division, Oak Ridge, Tennessee

The Liquid Carbonic Division, General Dynamics Corporation, 767 Industrial Road, San Carlos, California

Nuclear-Chicago Corporation, 223 West Erie St., Chicago 10, Illinois

Oak Ridge National Laboratory, Union Carbide Nuclear Company, Isotopes Division, Box X, Oak Ridge, Tennessee

General

Central Scientific Company, 1700 Irving Park Road, Chicago 13, Illinois

Chemical Rubber Company, 2310 Superior Ave., Cleveland 14, Ohio

Fisher Scientific Company, 711 Forbes Ave., Pittsburgh 19, Pennsylvania

Michigan Scientific Company, 6780 Jackson Ave., Ann Arbor, Michigan

Morris & Lee, 1685 Elmwood Ave., Buffalo, New York 14207

W. M. Welch Scientific Company, 1515 Sedgwich St., Chicago 10, Illinois

United Scientific Company, 200 North Jefferson, Chicago 6, Illinois

The *Thomas Register* lists manufacturers by categories and can be used to locate suppliers for particular projects. This register is available at most libraries.

further reading

~~~~~~~~~~~~~~~~~~~~~~~~~~~~~~~~

Books

A few of these books are meant for the professional but may be useful in any case.

Alexander, Peter, *Atomic Radiation and Life* (Penguin Books, Baltimore, 1957)

Asimov, Isaac, *Inside the Atom* (Abelard-Schuman, New York, 1961)

Bleich, Alan R., *The Story of X-Rays: from Röntgen to Isotopes* (Dover, New York, 1960)

Brown, J. G., *X-Rays and Their Applications* (Plenum Press, New York, 1966)

Clark, George L., *Applied X-Rays* (McGraw-Hill, New York, 1955)

————, *Encyclopedia of X-Rays and Gamma Rays* (Reinhold, New York, 1963)

Dibner, Bern, *Wilhelm Conrad Röntgen and the Discovery of X Rays* (Watts, New York, 1968)

Dogigli, Johannes, *The Magic of Rays* (Knopf, New York, 1961)

Esterer, Arnulf K., *Discoverer of X-Ray: Wilhelm Konrad Röntgen* (Messner, New York, 1968)

152

General Electric Co., *Principles of X-Ray Generation* (booklet)

————, *The Story of X-Ray* (booklet, 1963; both obtainable from G.E. at 4855 Electric Ave., Milwaukee, Wis. 53201)

Glasser, Otto, *Dr. W. C. Röntgen* (Charles C Thomas, Springfield, Illinois, 1958)

Guinier, A., *X-Ray Studies of Materials* (Wiley, New York, 1963)

Hart, Alan L., *Those Mysterious Rays* (Harper, New York, 1943)

Jaworski, Irene D., and Alexander Joseph, *Atomic Energy* (Harcourt Brace, New York, 1961)

Lytel, Allan H., *Industrial X-Ray Handbook* (Howard Sams, Indianapolis, 1963)

McKown, Robin, *The Fabulous Isotopes* (Holiday House, New York, 1962)

Rossi, Bruno B., *Cosmic Rays* (McGraw-Hill, New York, 1964)

Schubert, Jack, and Ralph E. Lapp, *Radiation: What It Is and How It Affects You* (Viking, New York, 1957)

Stong, C. L., *The Scientific American Book of Projects for the Amateur Scientist* (Simon & Schuster, New York, 1960)

Turtox Service Leaflet No. 53, *Experiments in Radiobiology* (General Biological Supply House, 8200 S. Hoyne Ave., Chicago, Ill., 60620)

Wilson, A. J. C., *X-Ray Optics* (Barnes & Noble, New York, 1949)

Worsnop, B. L., and F. C. Chalkin, *X Rays* (Wiley, New York, 1950)

Yates, Raymond F., *Atomic Experiments for Boys* (Harper, New York, 1952)

Pamphlets by U. S. Atomic Energy Commission

(From USAEC, P. O. Box 62, Oak Ridge, Tennessee 37830)

Atoms in Agriculture
Experiments with Radiation on Seeds (Nos. 1 & 2)
Food Preservation by Irradiation
The Genetic Effects of Radiation
Nondestructive Testing
Radioisotope Experiments in High School Biology
Radioisotopes and Life Processes
Radioisotopes in Industry
Radioisotopes in Medicine
What Can You Expect from Atomic-Irradiated Seeds?
Your Body and Radiation

Magazine Articles

Berland, Theodore, "Roentgen's Magic Rays" (*Today's Health*, March 1967)

DeBenedetti, Sergio, "The Mössbauer Effect" (*Scientific American*, April 1960)

Kirkpatrick, Paul, "The X-Ray Microscope" (*Scientific American*, March 1949)

Muller, H. J., "Radiation and Human Mutation" (*Scientific American*, November 1955)

Platzman, Robert L., "What Is Ionizing Radiation?" *Scientific American*, September 1959)

Reber, Grote, "Radio Astronomy" (*Scientific American*, September 1949)

Smith, J. C., Kimeldorf, D. J., and E. L. Hunt, "Motor Responses of Moths to Low-Intensity X-ray Exposure" (*Science*, May 17, 1963)

Sonneborn, T. M., "H. J. Muller, Crusader for Human Betterment" (*Science*, November 15, 1968)

index

absorptometry, 66
Aerobee rocket, 77-78
alpha rays, 48
altimeters, 93-94
angstrom unit, 26
astronomy, 70-79
  gamma-ray, 79-80
  satellites, 80
  X-ray, 70-79
atomic energy, radiation dangers, 107-108
atoms, 54

Baade, Walter, 76
background radiation, *see* natural radiation
Becquerel, Antoine, 46-50, 99-100
Becquerel's rays, *see* radioactive rays
beta rays, 48
biological effects, 89-116

birth defects, 115
botany experiments, 143
  see also plants
Brown, Frank A., 99

cancer treatment, 58, 106
cathode-ray tube, homemade, 139
cathode rays, 33-39, 55
  producing, 139-140
cell damage, 99-109
  stages, 102
chest X rays, 82, 104
chromosomes, 109-111
Clark, George W., 80
cloud chamber
  experiment, 135-137
  homemade, 135-136
cobalt bomb, 61
cobalt therapy, 61
color television, radiation from, 107